Biophysics and Cybernetic Systems

Proceedings of the Second Cybernetic Sciences Symposium

Edited by

MYLES MAXFIELD
University of Southern California

ARTHUR CALLAHAN
Office of Naval Research

LAWRENCE J. FOGEL
General Dynamics

October 13, 1964
Sponsored by the Office of Naval Research and
the Allan Hancock Foundation

1965
SPARTAN BOOKS, Inc.
Washington, D.C.

MACMILLAN AND CO., LTD.
London

PREFACE

This book contains material presented and discussed at the Second Cybernetic Sciences Symposium which convened in October 1964 under the sponsorship of the Office of Naval Research. The symposium was hosted by the Allan Hancock Foundation, University of Southern California, Los Angeles, California. Its theme: *Biophysics and the Cybernetic Sciences.*

This was the second in a series of invitational symposia which are intended to provide a forum for the presentation and critical analysis of significant research currently in progress at selected laboratories. Each of these symposia focuses attention on a particular subject area within the cybernetic sciences. The first Cybernetic Sciences Symposium was held at the Willis Booth Computing Center, California Institute of Technology, in November of 1963. Its theme was *Self-Organizing Systems.* The papers presented before this symposium appear in a book entitled, *Self-Organizing Systems, 1963,** edited by Dr. James Emmett Garvey.

The Second Cybernetic Sciences Symposium was jointly organized by the Physical Science Division (the Biophysics Program of the Physics Branch), the Mathematical Science Division (the Information System Branch), and the Biological Science Division (the Biophysics Program of the Medicine and Denistry Branch). Here is testimony to the integrative effect of Cybernetics. The five technical sessions of this symposium further reflect the interdisciplinary viewpoint. The first session entitled, *The Biophysics of Membranes,* was chaired by Dr. Myles Maxfield of USC, the second entitled, *Neural Network Modeling,* was chaired by Dr. R. David

---

* Published by the Office of Naval Research, Department of the Navy, Washington, D. C., Document Number ACR 96.

i

Joseph of Douglas Astropower Laboratories, the third entitled, *Biological Modeling,* was chaired by Prof. George P. Moore of UCLA, and the last session entitled, *Theories of Self-Organizing Systems,* was chaired by Dr. Lawrence J. Fogel of General Dynamics/Astronautics. The audience included specialists in a wide variety of specialities—biology, physiology, immunology, psychology, physics, communication engineering, computer sciences, and mathematics.

Each of the symposia in this series concludes with a Review and Analysis Session. Here the informal atmosphere encourages objective discussion between the authors and the audience. Some of the more pertinent commentaries of this session appear in this book. This session was moderated by Dr. James Emmett Garvey of ONR/Pasadena Office.

The Editors would like to express their sincere appreciation to the participants of this Symposium, whose contributions of time and effort have made possible a most stimulating and inspiring discussion of recent advances in the exciting and dynamic field of Cybernetics.

In particular we should like to thank the representatives of the host institution, Dr. Norman Topping, President of the University of Southern California and Dr. Leslie Chambers, Director of the Allan Hancock Foundation.

Additional expressions of gratitude are due to Dr. Martin Garstens and Mr. Donald Pollack of the Office of Naval Research, Washington, D. C., for their cooperation and help in the organization of this Symposium, and to Dr. James Emmett Garvey of the Office of Naval Research Branch Office, Pasadena, for his essential contributions to its success.

CONTENTS

FOREWORD

This symposium on Cybernetics offers a measure of the level of advancement of a new science which draws upon various classical disciplines in order to bring together information concerning communication and control in living organisms. The symposium was held at the Allan Hancock Foundation of the University of Southern California . . . a particularly appropriate place in that this foundation is primarily concerned with gaining a greater insight and understanding of the biophysical functioning of living matter.

Reflecting this general orientation, the papers presented before the symposium ranged from those which directly relate to the detailed functioning of biological systems all the way to those which are concerned with the development of formal representations of systems which display some of the properties peculiar to living systems. For example, at one end of the spectrum, Pape describes an investigation of the molecular structure of cell membrances, which are sensitive elements in a cybernetic system; Binggeli devotes his attention to the functional properties of bilaterally symmetric brains.

It is characteristic of biology that research progresses simultaneously at various levels. To a large extent such concurrent inquiry is appropriate in view of the relative absence of quantitative theories which afford a unification of knowledge over the various levels. From the biologists' point of view, cybernetics is the attempt to develop such formal concepts which will make it possible to deduce the existence of unexpected properties at each level even in the absence of complete information at that level. In a very real sense the purpose of cybernetics is to provide a gestalt over the various levels of inquiry.

Considering biological systems as functional entities, it is of interest to inquire into their properties of homeostasis and the more general aspects

v

of goal-seeking. Several papers at this symposium were devoted to such problems. Stewart describes experiments in which the gross properties of large numbers of interconnected neuron-like elements are explored. Asendorf indicates the result of experiments performed within a logical system which learns through the assimilation of punishment and reward. Bremermann et al discussed various techniques for goal-seeking within a domain subject to linear constraints. Fogel et al describe the fast-time evolution of finite state machines through iterative mutation and selection in order to discover successively improved logic for goal-seeking within the given environment. Gold discusses some of the formal implications of automata theory in terms of the limits of identifiability of languages and some of the related implications of these limits on the ability of a goal-seeker.

Other papers address subjects which fall between these extremes. Although the authors demonstrate great individuality of approach, their interests are unified by the common concern for the cross-fertilization of ideas. This symposium has achieved one of its major aims if those who actively engage in research relevant to cybernetics will come to better understand one another. A prerequisite to the goal of cybernetics is concise language within each specialty, and at the same time, a sufficient semantic base for effective inter-communications across the related disciplines.

It is important that those who are well aware of detailed discoveries in the biological sciences accept the more formal investigations as being essential, in spite of the fact that there may be a considerable time lag before such research *pays off*. Certainly knowledge begins with empirical evidence, but the large steps are made when the scientific method can be employed in order to guide the investigation. The great complexity of the real-world precludes trial and search as an efficient means for the discovery of new information. Cybernetics requires the use of models which depict the relationship among data as well as the data themselves. Mathematics provides a wide variety of representations which can be used for the construction of models . . . theories, conjectures, hypotheses, which serve to direct the attention of the investigator. When these are verified, they provide a greater depth of understanding in terms of the functional attributes of the system which is being modeled.

Living systems are bound within an interactive environment. The search for new knowledge rests upon the acceptance that physical laws govern this entire domain . . . including both animate and inanimate systems. The peculiarities of living systems are the result of their internal organization. Their behavior is as subject to analysis and understanding as is the structure and behavior of other physical matter.

This symposium is the second in a series. It is always easy to point to deficiencies. Cybernetics is a new science. Although individual achievements may be of limited scope, a major benefit has already been achieved . . . the interaction of those who seriously address the problems of communication and control in living systems. The future of mankind strongly depends upon the gaining of just such knowledge and its wise utilization.

MYLES MAXFIELD
LAWRENCE J. FOGEL

1

A GLYCOPROTEIN ASSOCIATED WITH CELL MEMBRANES*

Leon Pape† and Myles Maxfield

Allan Hancock Foundation
University of Southern California
Los Angeles, California

Robert Hooke's postulation of cells as the fundamental unit of physiological systems was based on the observation of the rigid structural remnants of cork cells, namely the cell walls. Since that time, the investigation of cell physiology has been concerned at least as much with the structure, biosynthesis, and function of cell membranes as with any other subcellular unit and possibly all the others combined.

Much progress has been made in elucidating the nature of the cell membrane but, in spite of the gaps which have been filled in, fundamental questions remain to be answered.

Unlike the need to climb Mt. Everest *just because it's there,* the need to understand the structure and function of the cell membrane is dictated by the fact that the cell membrane, in addition to providing structural integrity to the cell, is vitally involved in the transport of information which is critical to the existence of the organ.

This is most obvious in the neuron where membranes are not only

* Supported by Grant #AI-04873-02, National Institute of Allergy and Infectious Diseases, National Institutes of Health.

† Present Address: Physics Department, California State College at Los Angeles, Los Angeles, California.

1

involved in the transport of information via electrical signals along the axon, but mediate the neuro-humoral interaction at the end plate.

In 1935, Danielli and Davson postulated the classical membrane model. This structural concept was based on investigation of lipid solubility and surface tension. In 1957, Robertson proposed a modified concept which has now been characterized as the unit membrane. Figure 1 shows

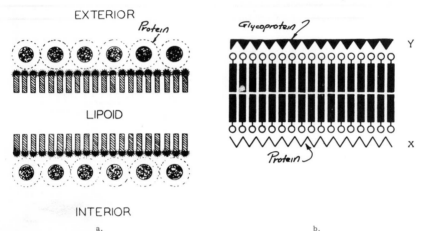

Figure 1. Membrane models
    a) Danielli-Davson
    b) Unit Membrane

Reproduced from "Biophysics of Physiological and Pharmacological Actions." American Association for the Advancement of Science (1961).

schematic representations of the Danielli-Davson and unit membrane models. These membranes have been well visualized with the aid of the electron microscope as seen in Fig. 2. Furthermore, using the resolving power of the microscope, the nature of the myelin system of nerve fibers or axons has been explored and appears to be the extension of the mesaxon. The development of the myelin system is demonstrated in Figs. 3 and 4.

Another system in which the cell acts to transport information in the same manner, but for a different purpose, is the kidney tubular cell. Here the operation of an energy-requiring system, in conjunction with the cell membrane, maintains an ionic level against a concentration gradient and protects the electrolyte and fluid balance of the organism. Again we find unit membranes, both within the cytoplasm and separating the cytoplasm from the extracellular space. Figure 5 is a low power view of the proximal convoluted tubule of the guinea pig nephron. A high power view of the basalar portion reveals the characteristic structure of the

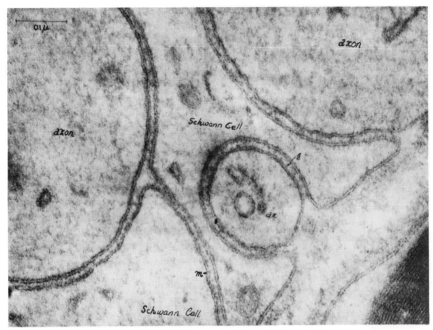

Figure 2. Electron micrograph of nerve fibers. Relationship between Schwann cells and individual axons is demonstrated. A developing mesaxon (M) can be seen.

Reproduced from "Biophysics of Physiological and Pharmacological Actions." American Association for the Advancement of Science (1961).

membrane as shown in Fig. 6. The protein layers have been stained dark by osmium tetroxide while the central lipid section, which does not stain, appears to be transparent to the electron beam.

Our interest has been directed at the protein moiety which constitutes the external layer of the unit membrane. That is, the component which appears to have the structure of a glycoprotein.

In 1951 Tamm and Horsfall isolated a component of normal human urine which upon analysis was identified as a glycoprotein. Subsequent investigation of this T & H glycoprotein has shown it to be made of monomeric structures consisting of two heterosaccharide groups covalently bound to a protein moiety. In its natural form the molecule is a polymer of these units with a molecular weight of 7×10^6. It is also found naturally as an aggregation of four 7×10^6 units, two side by side and two end to end. Figure 7 is an elctron micrograph of the T & H urinary glycoprotein. In this sample both 7×10^6 and 28×10^6 units are visible.

Efforts to localize the cellular source for this glycoprotein have been

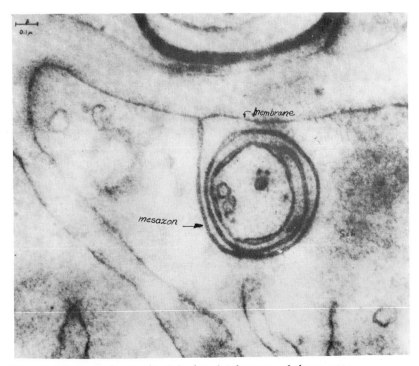

Figure 3. Electron micrograph of further development of the mesaxon.
Reproduced from "Biophysics of Physiological and Pharmacological Actions." American Association for the Advancement of Science (1961).

unsuccessful in the past. The possibility that the macromolecule is elaborated in the goblet cells of the urinary tract and extruded as mucinous material was ruled out by experiments which showed that T & H glycoprotein could be extracted from as high as the kidney pelvis. Goblet cells in man do not appear higher than the trigone of the bladder.

Experiments using histological stains like PAS and fluorescent antibodies, while suggesting that the site might be along the luminal border of the nephron, as well as in cytoplasmic granules, were not unambiguous.

In order to resolve this problem and shed some light on the relationship between the T & H glycoprotein and the surface layer of the cell membrane, ferritin labeled antibodies were employed in conjunction with electron microscopy.

Antibodies against guinea pig T & H glycoprotein produced in rabbit serum were conjugated with ferritin and then incubated with fresh sections of guinea pig kidney. These sections were then washed, fixed in osmium tetroxide and embedded in methacrylate. Figure 8 is an electron micro-

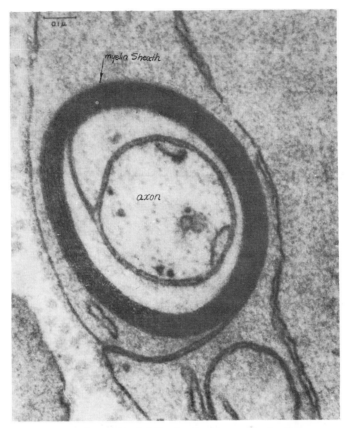

Figure 4. Electron micrograph of fully developed myelin sheath.
Reproduced from "Biophysics of Physiological and Pharmacological Actions." American Association for the Advancement of Science (1961).

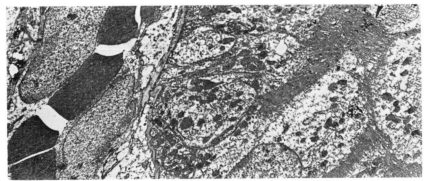

Figure 5. Low power view, proximal convoluted tubule of the guinea pig nephron (cell nuclei (N) and brush border (BB) can be seen.) ($\times$ 8,000)

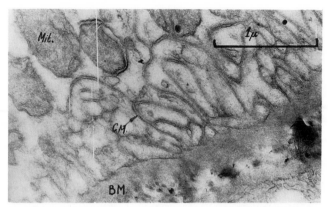

Figure 6. Basalar position proximal tubular cell. The basement membrane (BM), cell membrane (CM) and mitochondria (Mit) can be seen. (× 48,000)

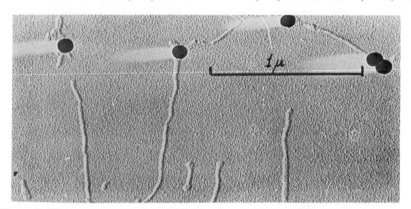

Figure 7. Electron micrograph of T & H urinary glycoprotein. (× 55,000)

graph of a pure solution of ferritin sprayed on a specimen grid. A high power view of control untreated proximal tubule brush border is shown in Fig. 9. Figure 10 is a view of brush border in kidney tissue treated with the antibody ferritin conjugate. The presence of ferritin granules is apparent. Figures 11 and 12 show comparable regions of proximal tubule endoplasmic reticulum in treated and untreated tissue specimens.

Control tissues consisting of non-incubated tissue, tissue incubated in pure antibody and then conjugated antibody and tissue incubated with ferritin alone were also examined. No evidence of ferritin incorporation was noted in the latter two samples. Furthermore, except for occasional ferritin molecules along the luminal border of the distal tubules, no other kidney sections examined showed ferritin incorporation.

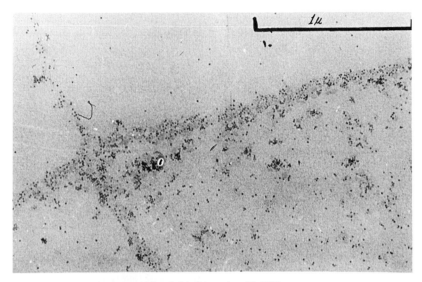

Figure 8. Electron micrograph of ferritin. ($\times$ 90,000)

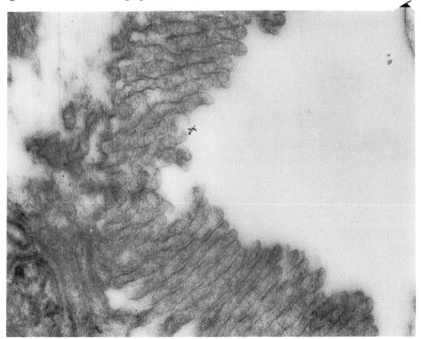

Figure 9. Proximal tubule brush border (untreated). ($\times$ 80,000)

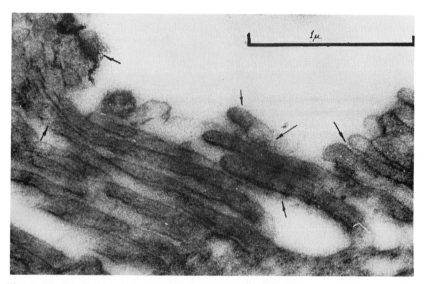

Figure 10. Proximal tubule brush border treated with antibody ferritin conjugate. Ferritin granules are indicated by arrows. ($\times$ 90,000)

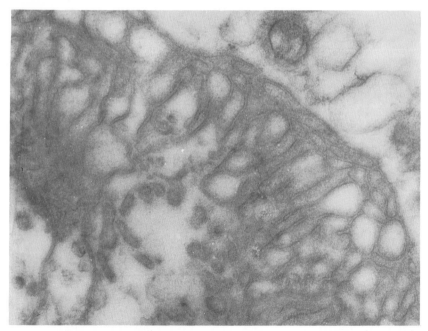

Figure 11. Electron micrograph of the smooth region of the endoplasmic reticulum (untreated). ($\times$ 80,000)

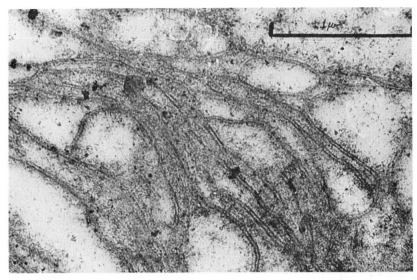

Figure 12. Electron micrograph of smooth region of the endoplasmic reticulum. Tissue has been treated with merritin antibody conjugate. Ferritin granules are plainly visible. (× 90,000)

It is therefore reasonable to postulate that the T & H glycoprotein is elaborated in the endoplasmic reticulum. From this site it is extruded onto the brush border of the proximal tubule as the surface component of the cell membrane. Its presence in the urine reflects the natural attrition or mechanical abrasion which occurs in the nephron.

2

BIMOLECULAR LIPID MEMBRANES

CARL D'AGOSTINO, JR. and LONNIE SMITH, JR.
Aeronutronic Research Laboratory
Newport Beach, California

INTRODUCTION

The role played by the cell membrane in biological activity can not be overemphasized, for, as the phase boundary of the cell, it must constitute a central element in active transport, sensory perception, neural communication, enzymatic activity and virtually all phenomena associated with life. Although a great deal is known about the physiological behavior of cell membranes, an adequate description of the chemical and physical behavior at the molecular level has not been developed.

Overton (1895) found that lipid molecules penetrated the cell membrane readily and thus he implied that membranes are composed of lipids or lipid-like molecules. The physical arrangement of the lipid molecules was first suggested by Gorter and Grendel (1925) who extracted the lipids from red blood cells and found that when spread as a monolayer at an air-water interface, they occupied an area approximately twice that of the cell surface area from which they were extracted. They concluded that the membrane is composed of a bimolecular layer of lipids. Based on this earlier work and on permeability measurements Davson and Danielli (1943) proposed the model shown in Fig. 1 which is accepted as the basic structure of the cell membrane. This model consists of two layers of phospholipid molecules (Fig. 6 shows a typical phospholipid, phosphatidyl ethanolamine) arranged with their hydrophobic, long hydrocarbon chains toward one

11

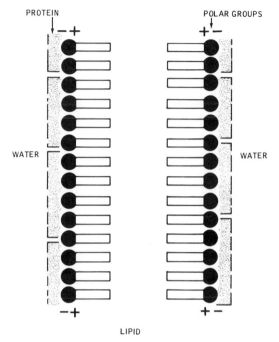

Figure 1. Model of cell membrane proposed by Davson and Danielli.

another and with the hydrophilic, polar end groups facing outward toward the surrounding aqueous media. Each side of the bimolecular lipid is postulated to be covered with a layer of protein. The general chemical composition of this model is consistent with the measurements of Williams et al (1941) and Lehninger et al (1958) which have shown the cell membranes to be made up principally of protein, phospholipid and cholesterol (a neutral lipid).

Direct observations made by X-ray diffraction and more recently by electron microscopy have allowed Robertson (1964) to modify the Davson and Danielli model. The transverse dimension of about 75 Å , measured for many natural membranes, supports the concept of a bimolecular arrangement. However, spatial considerations suggest that the protein associated with the membrane is spread as a fully opened monomolecular layer rather than as globular molecules, as had been suggested by Davson and Danielli. The different chemical reactivities of the outside and inside strata of the membrane to fixing agents used in electron microscopy has led Robertson to postulate that the membrane is chemically asymmetric.

Correlation of cell membrane phenomena with cell structure has been exceedingly slow, both because of the difficulty of experimentation *in situ* and because of the poorly defined chemical and physical composition of the system. Recently, Mueller et al (1962 a, b, 1963, 1964) and Mueller and Rudin (1963) have reported the formation of membranes 60 to 90 Å thick in aqueous solution from a complex mixture of phospholipids and neutral lipids extracted from beef brain. By adsorbing an unknown substance, thought to be a protein, on the membrane they have produced a membrane system with very unique electrical properties which in many respects stimulates the behavior of natural cell membranes. This system overcomes many of the experimental difficulties of working with the natural membrane; however, the chemical and physical complexities remain.

This paper will discuss some studies made on membranes formed from beef brain lipids using the techniques described by Mueller, et al. (1963a, 1964). It will then discuss some very preliminary studies on membranes formed from relatively pure lipids of known composition.

EXPERIMENTAL

MEMBRANE FORMATION

All membranes discussed in this study were formed in a cell similar to that described by Mueller et al (1963a). The cell consists of two concentric chambers; the outer one a 40 ml glass petri dish approximately 5 cm in diameter, the inner one a 4 ml polyethylene cup approximately 1.5 cm in diameter. A small section in the side of the polyethylene cup is thinned to about 0.1 mm by heating the wall and blowing out a small bubble. A 1 mm polished hole is pierced in the thinned section of the wall with a heated needle. Both compartments of the cell are filled with identical 0.1 N NaCl solutions buffered with 0.005 N histidine until the hole in the polyethylene cup is about 0.5 cm below the surface of the solutions. The cell is placed on a warming plate and allowed to come to temperature. All measurements are made at $37 \pm 1\,^{\circ}$C.

Membranes are formed by brushing a dilute solution of the lipids in chloroform-methanol solvent across the hole in the polyethylene cup with a very fine sable hair brush. As the solvent evaporates into the surrounding aqueous solution, the lipid layer gradually thins until an abrupt transition occurs. Very sharply defined, optically *black* spots appear in the lipid layer which increase in size until they merge and cover the entire area of the hole except for an annulus around the black area, which is apparently excess lipid that has been extruded toward the circumference during membrane formations. This formation is completely analogous to the formation of so-called *black* soap films described by Overbeek (1960). Membrane formation is observed with a low power microscope in light reflected by the lipid layer from a microscope projection lamp.

ELECTRICAL MEASUREMENTS

The dc current-voltage characteristics of the membranes were measured by reading the current in series with the membrane with a Hewlett-Packard model 425A microvolt-ammeter and the potential drop across the membrane with a Keithly model 610BR electrometer. The electrodes were fiber-tipped calomel electrodes which have been found to introduce an emf of less than 1 mv into the circuit. The potentials across the membranes were supplied by a 1.5 volt dry cell and a potentiometer all mounted on teflon to reduce the effects of leakage currents. Several load-limiting resistors may be switched in series with the emf source allowing it to act as a constant current source, a constant voltage source, or several intermediate combinations. The entire apparatus and its associated leads was carefully shielded to reduce the effects of ac pickup. Measurements on a blank polyethylene cup revealed no leakage currents for voltages up to 500 mv.

Capacitance measurements on the membranes were made with a General Radio capacitance measuring assembly employing a Schering-type bridge and an oscillator covering the range 10 cps to 100 kc. Fiber-tipped calomel electrodes were used to measure capacitances. The capacitance of a blank cup, the electrodes and leads was measured to be about 200 $\mu\mu$f.

MATERIALS

Lipids were extracted in chloroform-methanol solution (2:1 v/v) from beef brain white matter using the modified method of Folch and Lees (1951) described by Mueller et al (1963a). They found that in addition to the lipid extract, liquid hydrocarbons, such as silicon fluid, tetradecane, *a*-tocopherol, or mineral oil, are required to allow good membrane formation. These additives are reported to prevent solidification of the membranes which results from excessively rapid loss of chloroform-methanol during formation. In addition, cholesterol has been found to increase the dielectric strength of the membranes. The following solution suggested by Mueller et al (1963a) was therefore used to prepare brain lipid membranes: 2% beef brain extract, 2% cholesterol; 15-20% *a*-tocopherol in 2:1 chloroform-methanol solution.

Single phospholipids and neutral lipids were obtained commercially in the best grade available from the suppliers. The phospholipids, phosphatidyl ethanolamine, phosphatidyl choline and phosphatidyl serine were obtained from Sigma Chemical Company. Phosphatidyl ethanolamine was also obtained from Mann Research Laboratories. The neutral lipids cholesterol, cholesteryl palmitate, cholesteryl stearate, and cholesteryl oleate were obtained from K & K Laboratories. Cholesterol was further purified by recrystallizing twice in ethanol.

ELECTRICALLY ACTIVE MEMBRANES

Mueller et al (1962a) reported the discovery of an unidentified water-soluble molecular species, probably a protein, which when adsorbed on a lipid membrane lowers the resistance by about two orders of magnitude and induces electrical *activity* in the sense that the membrane resistance shifts reversibly from one stable value to another in response to a super-imposed threshold voltage. This molecular species is obtained as the bi-product of the bacterial growth of *Aerobacter cloacae* (American Type Culture Collection, strain 961) in egg white medium. The activating molecular species has been prepared using the techniques described by Mueller and Rudin (private communication).

RESULTS AND DISCUSSION

MOLECULAR ARRANGEMENT OF THE LIPID MEMBRANES

Several recent papers suggest that membranes formed by complex mixtures of beef brain phospholipids or single phospholipids and hydrocarbons (or neutral lipids) exhibit a bimolecular structure. Mueller et al (1964) have reported a thickness of 60-90 Å for electron microscopic measurements of complex phospholipid—a-tocopherol membranes. Thompson (1964) and Thompson et al (1964) from optical measurements have reported thicknesses of about 60 Å for lecithin—n-tetradecane membranes. Haydon, et al. (1964) from capacitance measurements have reported thicknesses of 48 Å for the hydrocarbon part of lecithin—n-decanemembranes. These thicknesses are all consistent with the bimolecular concept.

In view of the apparent dimensions of the membrane, the high specific resistances ($\sim 10^8$ ohm-cm^2), the high specific capacitances (~ 0.5-μf/cm^2) and the high breakdown voltages (~ 150 mv or $\sim 3 \times 10^5$ v/cm) strongly suggest a highly ordered structure. Energetic considerations for long polar/nonpolar molecules would favor an arrangement whereby the long hydrophobic, hydrocarbon chains would be held toward one another through van der Waals' forces and the hydrophilic polar end groups attracted outward toward the surrounding polar aqueous media, thereby minimizing the free energy of the system. This arrangement is the same as that postulated by the Davson-Danielli model.

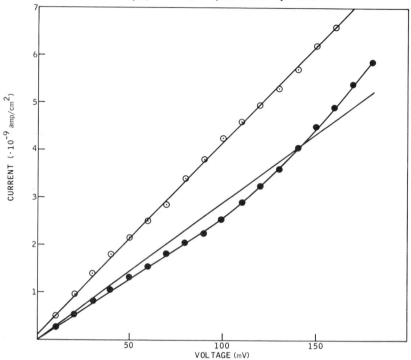

Figure 2. Current-voltage characteristics of membranes prepared from beef brain lipid extract.

MEMBRANES FORMED FROM BRAIN LIPIDS

Stable *black* membranes were formed from the beef brain lipid extract solution discussed earlier. The current-voltage curves for two typical membranes are shown in Fig. 2. The membranes exhibit very high resistances and while the specific resistances are not reproducible from membrane to membrane, they generally lie betwen 2×10^7 and 10^8 ohm-cm^2. The breakdown voltage is between 150 and 200 mv and the membranes obey Ohm's Law.

Addition of a few drops of a dilute solution of the activity-inducing molecule to either side of the membrane produced a sudden three-order of magnitude drop in resistance. The current-voltage characteristics as shown in Fig. 3 are now no longer ohmic but rather much like those of a tunnel diode with a large negative resistance region. Once the resistance has dropped and stabilized, the current-voltage curve is completely reversible. In addition, reversing the polarity of the applied potential simply reproduces the curve characteristics with current flow in the opposite direction. Because of the low breakdown voltage of the *activated* membranes

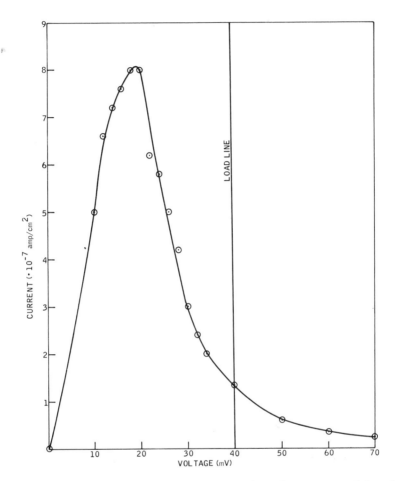

Figure 3. Current-voltage characteristics of *activated* membrance prepared from beef brain lipid extract.

(80-100 mv), all measurements were made with a constant voltage source. It can be seen that proper selection of the load line will enable the system to be *switched* much like a tunnel diode, thereby producing the reversible transient *action potentials* discussed by Mueller and Rudin (1963).

Thin layer chromatographic studies were run on the beef brain lipid extracts using techniques described by Randerath (1963) and Skipski et al (1962). The results showed at least seven distinct lipid components present in the lipid extract. The chemical complexity of the system makes further investigation undesirable.

MEMBRANES FORMED FROM KNOWN LIPIDS

The phospholipids, phosphatidyl enthanolamine, phosphatidyl choline, and phosphatidyl serine; the neutral lipids cholesterol, cholesteryl oleate, cholesteryl stearate, and cholesteryl plamitate; and *a*-tocopherol were all tested in various concentrations in chloroform-methanol first singly and then in various combinations for their ability to form stable membranes. Although many combinations showed evidence of *black* formation, the simplest stable membranes were formed from phosphatidyl ethanolamine (2% w/v), cholesteryl oleate (3% w/v) and *a*-tocopherol (15-20%-w/v). The long term stability of these membranes is in every case much less than that of the beef lipid membranes. All of the commercial phospholipids showed some discoloration which is often evidence of oxidation. Thin layer chromatographic studies of the commercial phospholipids using

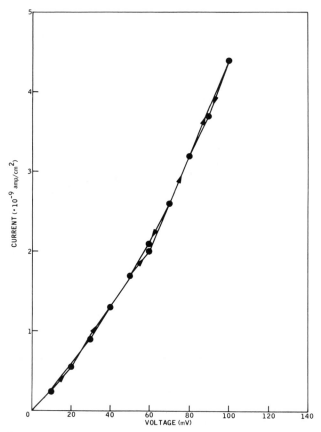

Figure 4. Current-voltage characteristics of phosphatidyl ethanolamine membranes.

the techniques by Randerath (1963) and Skipski et al (1962) further confirms the presence of impurities. Thompson et al (1964) have indicated that oxidation of the phospholipids may be a major factor in preventing formation of stable membranes.

The current-voltage characteristics of a typical membrane are shown in Fig. 4. The membranes are ohmic, with specific resistances of 2 to 6 X 10^7 ohm-cm^2 and breakdown voltages of about 100 mv.

Preliminary dielectric measurements at low frequency give a membrane specific capacitance of about 0.5 μf/cm^2 with a dissipation factor of about zero. If it is assumed that the dielectric constant of the membrane can be approximated by the value of 2.6 found by Crowe and Smyth (1951) for various triglycerides at 37°C, the thickness of the membrane is calculated to be 46 Å.

Addition of several drops of the activity inducing molecular species to one side of the membrane produced a sudden drop in specific resistance to about 2 X 10^4 ohm-cm^2. The current-voltage characteristics of the *activated* membrane are shown in Fig. 5. The general nature of the curve is quite similar to that obtained for the *activated* brain lipid membrane.

Attempts to make capacitance measurements or prolonged current-voltage measurements on the activated membrane have not been successful because of the relative instability of th *active* phosphatidyl ethanolamine-cholesteryl oleate—*a*-tocopherol membrane.

The approximately equimolecular proportions of phosphatidyl ethanolamine and cholesteryl oleate in the most stable membrane composition permits some interesting speculation. Finean (1953) noting that cholesterol is present in myelin as free cholesterol in approximately equimolecular proportions with the phospholipids suggested the formation of a complex involving the -OH group of the cholesterol and the polar end group of the phospholipid. Figure 6 shows a possible configuration of the complex. This complex would be stabilized by the van der Waals association of the hydrocarbon parts of the molecule and the polar interactions of the end groups, and would serve to accommodate the longest and shortest molecules in a stable layer of uniform thickness. This speculation, unfortunately, has not taken into consideration the very high concentration of *a*-tocopherol or hydrocarbon required to form stable membranes.

A very strong analogy can be seen in the current-voltage characteristics of phospholipid-neutral lipid membranes *activated* with an unknown molecular species and in the current-voltage measurements reported by Moore (1959) for the squid axon membrane as shown in Fig. 7. He has been able to show the large negative resistance region of the natural membrane with voltage clamp measurements and to simulate action potentials with current clamp measurements.

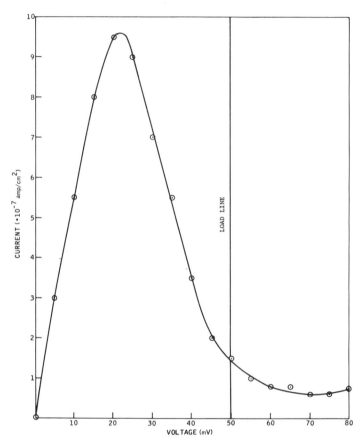

Figure 5. Current-voltage characteristics of *activated* phosphatidyl ethanolamine membrane.

CONCLUSIONS

This paper has discussed lipid membranes whose chemical and physical properties bear striking resemblance to natural cell membranes. A large number of unique physical and chemical parameters found only in the natural cell have been noted in a system which is not only much simpler than the cell membrane, but much more readily accessible to experimentation.

There is strong evidence that the phospholipid membranes exist in a bimolecular arrangement similar to that postulated by Davson and Danielli for the natural cell membrane. The recurring agreement for the thickness

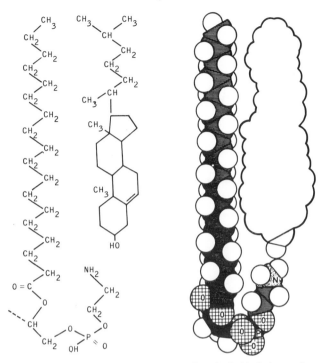

Figure 6. Probable spatial arrangement of phospholipid-cholesterol complex.

of the *black* structure from different measurements, combined with the knowledge of the type of molecules making up the membrane, and the highly ordered nature of the system provide a firm base for postulating a bilayer structure. The specific resistance of 2×10^4 ohm-cm^2 and specific capacitance of 0.5 μf/cm^2 measured for lipid membranes are in excellent agreement with specific resistances of 10^3-10^5 ohm-cm^2 and specific capacitances of 1 μf/cm^2 reported for natural membranes. The extremely high dielectric strength of the phospholipid membranes, in excess of 2×10^5 V/cm, is again a characteristic of many natural membranes. The general diode-like shape of the current-voltage curve of *activated* membranes is in remarkable agreement with the current-voltage curve measured by the voltage clamp method for the squid axon membrane.

BIBLIOGRAPHY

R. W. Crowe and C. P. Smyth, *J.A.C.S.*, *73*, 2040, 1951.

H. Davson and J. F. Danielli, *The Permeability of Natural Membranes*, Univ. Press, Cambridge, 1943.

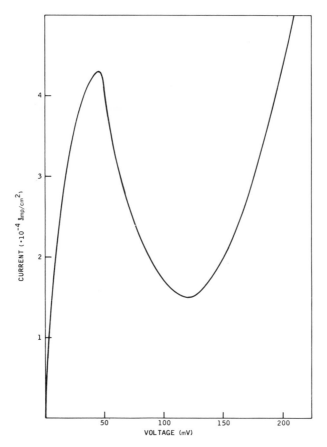

Figure 7. Current-voltage characteristics of natural membrane obtained from the squid giant axon. [From Moore (1959)].

J B. Finean, *Exptl. Cell Res., 5,* 202, 1953.

J. Folch and M. Lees, *J. Biol. Chem.,* 191, 807, 1951.

E. Gorter and R. Grendal, *J. Exptl. Med., 41,* 439, 1925.

D. A. Haydon, T. Hanai and J. Taylor, *Proc. Roy. Soc., A 281,* 377, 1964.

A. L. Lehninger, C. L. Wadkins, C. Cooper, T. M. Devlin and J. L. Gamable, *Science, 128,* 450, 1958.

J. W. Moore, *Nature, 183,* 265, 1959.

P. Mueller and D. O. Rudin, H. Ti Tien and W. C. Westcott, *Circulation, 26,* 1167, 1962a.

P. Mueller and D. O. Rubin, *J. Theoret Biol., 4,* 268, 1963.

P. Mueller, D. O. Rudin, H. Ti Tien and W. C. Westcott, *Nature, 194,* 979, 1962b.

P. Mueller, D. O. Rudin, H. Ti Tien and W C. Westcott, *J. Phys. Chem., 67,* 534, 1963a.

P. Mueller, D. O. Rudin, H. Ti Tien and W. C. Westcott, *Recent Progress in Surface Science,* vol. 1, ed. by J. F. Danielli, K. G. A. Pankhurst and A. C. Riddiford, pp. 379-393, Academic Press, New York, 1964.

J. T. G. Overbeek, *J. Phys. Chem., 64,* 1178, 1960.

E. Overton, *Vischr. Naturf., Ges Zurich, 40,* 149, 1895.

K. Randerath, *Thin Layer Chromatography,* Academic Press, New York, 1963.

J. D. Robertson, *Cellular Membranes in Development,* ed. by M. Locke, pp. 1-81, Academic Press, New York, 1964.

V. P. Skipski, R. F. Peterson and M. Barclay, *J. Lipid Res., 3,* 467, 1962.

T. E. Thompson, *Cellular Membranes in Development,* ed. by M Locke, pp. 83-95, Academic Press, New York, 1964.

T. E. Thompson, C. Huang and L. Wheeldon, *J. Mol. Biol., 8,* 148, 1964.

H. H. Williams, B. N. Erickson and I. G. Macy, *Quart, Rev. Biol., 16,* 80, 1941.

3

PROGRESS IN EXPERIMENTAL RESEARCH ON ELECTROCHEMICAL ADAPTIVE SYSTEMS*

R. M. Stewart

*Space-General Corporation
El Monte, California*

BACKGROUND AND INTRODUCTION

At the First Cybernetic Sciences Symposium (on Self-Organizing Systems), held a year ago in Pasadena, I described theoretical and experimental work concerning simple inorganic electrochemical neural models.[1] There is a double-barreled motivation for this work: (a) technological, and (b) biological.

On the technological side we are hopeful of a breakthrough of the *complexity* barrier.[2] We believe that it is possible to construct a pliable electrochemical machine to be used for such things as pattern recognition, in which the fine structure and packing density of cells compares favorably with that of the brain. That this should be possible in an electrochemical system rests primarily with three unique characteristics:

(a) Distributed energy supply for signal impulse propagation (a la *Lillie iron-wire nerve model),*

* Further details on the work described in this paper may be found in Air Force Avionics Laboratory Technical Documentary Report No. AL TDR 64-254, "Research on Electrochemical Adaptive Systems," available from the Defense Documentation Center or Office of Technical Services, Department of Commerce. The work reported in this paper was supported in part by the United States Air Force Avionics Laboratory (WPAFB, Ohio), by the Office of Naval Research, and by the Space-General Corporation Independent Research and Development Program.

25

(b) Fine structure or *dendrite* growth by electrodeposition and corresponding *plasticity* of function, and

(c) Intrinsic active metal surface behavior which results in hypersensitivity to gross electrical control fields or massive shocks in recently active regions as compared to recently passive regions.

On the biological side, interest centers on the possibility of developing a meaningful model technique for the study of the behavior of large cell assemblies, especially with respect to the parallel questions of:

(a) Intercellular wave propagation and interactions, "synaptic transmission," and ephemeral memory,

(b) Long-term memory substrate, and

(c) Learning mechanisms.

A year ago we described basic electrochemical experiments which demonstrate plausible mechanisms for each of these physiological and psychological phenomena. I also pointed out that we were beginning construction of a special apparatus (called the Controlled Liquid Environment Facility, see Fig. 1) which we believed would bring available speed of response and recovery, lifetime and complexity within the realm of experimental feasibility. This was to be done by providing a stiff, sealed shell with means for raising both temperature (to 100°C) and pressure (to 2000 psi) and for exchanging fluids between the test chamber and a closed reservoir system. This apparatus has now been completed and has been in operation for several months. In the following paragraphs we will describe briefly some recent experimental results which have been obtained with the aid of this apparatus.

STABILITY SURVEY

The primary reason that the Controlled Liquid Environment Facility (CLEF) was built was to stabilize the transient reactions between iron and nitric acid which are responsible for the basic energy supply and signal transmission phenomena in our electrochemical neural models. Early experiments along these lines were plagued by unpredictable but frequent and violent instabilities. This instability was accompanied by voluminous bubble generation and was shown sometime ago to be triggered and sustained by the formation of bubbles on the surface of the iron. Rudimentary experiments had shown that stable waves could be generated at will simply by encapsulating the structure with its surrounding fluid at a slightly ele-

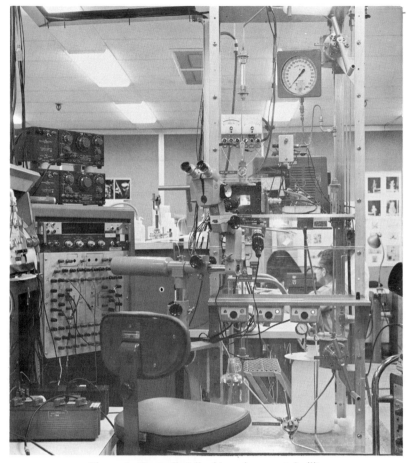

Figure 1. Controlled liquid environment facility.

vated pressure. Thus, following initial checks of mechanical and hydraulic integrity of the CLEF system, a series of tests was conducted in an effort to establish critical pressures required for stability over a range of temperatures and acid concentrations. Two series of tests were conducted, one using a single cell having a surface area of about .1 cm^2 and, secondly, with a small cluster of 14 iron pellets each pellet having a diameter of 2 mm. The single cell experimental structure is shown in Fig. 2. The electrode on the left is an insulated iron rod (about 3 mm diameter) whose end has been cut off and exposed to the surrounding acid; the center electrode is a gold high-impedance voltage reference electrode used to detect breakdown and recovery of the iron oxide membrane; and the third electrode

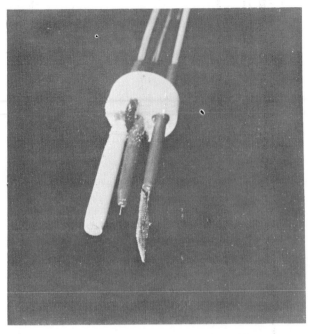

Figure 2. Single cell response assembly.

(on the right) is a platinum screen used to supply stimulus current. Wires attached to each of these three electrodes pass through an umbilical cord to the outside of the chamber where they can be connected to stimulus and monitoring equipment. The procedure used consisted of starting at a pressure sufficiently high to maintain stability and then repeatedly stimulating the cell at lower and lower pressures until a stimulus resulted in a clear instability. The results of these tests for the single cell are shown on Fig. 3. The critical pressures found with the cell cluster were of the same order of magnitude, although generally slightly higher. With all electrolytes investigated it was found that stable operation could be maintained up to a temperature of 100°C as long as the pressure was at least 400 psi. If the temperature does not exceed 70°C, pressure required for acid concentrations above 50% is approximately 100 psi. Stability was demonstrated over a wide range of concentrations and it appeared that there is a fairly critical concentration at about 45% HNO_3 (by weight) which, at any temperature, requires the highest stabilizing pressure. This factor, in addition to visual observations, seemed to indicate that a basically different passivation phenomenon occurs in two (high and low) concentration regimes.

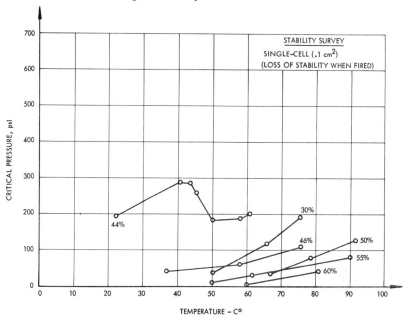

Figure 3. Single cell loss of stability.

SPEED OF RESPONSE AT HIGH TEMPERATURES

Subsequent to the stability survey described above, a series of determinations of single cell refractory period or recovery time were made at various concentrations and temperatures. The results of repetitive firing of a single cell are summarized in Fig. 4. It may be seen from these data points that the fastest recovery time recorded was approximately 5 msec at a temperature of 88 °C. At the time of these tests it was not possible to determine faster responses due to limitations on the speed of operation of our stimulus circuits. But it appears by extrapolation that it should be possible to obtain recovery times of 1 msec or 1 Kc pulsing rates at a temperature of about 100 °C. It has thus been demonstrated that we can achieve pulsing rates and recovery times comparable to the fastest human nerve cells. In most experimental work of the past, including Lillie's, a typical recovery time was about 15 minutes. Relative to those techniques, then, we have increased the speed of operation by a factor of approximately one million. Such speed increases are directly related to possible data rates in electrochemical data processing systems and are of fundamental importance not only from an engineering standpoint but also for the purpose of investigating complex cell assembly learning processes within a reasonable period of time.

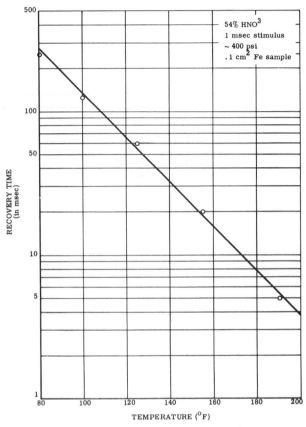

Figure 4. Effect of temperature on speed of recovery.

FIELD INDUCED GROWTH IN DENSE AGGREGATES

We expect the construction of high-density experimental cell assemblies to require two basic initial steps: (a) mixing of a fine aggregate consisting of glass and metal *seeds* followed by, (b) *maturation* procedures in which different liquids are introduced sequentially into the aggregate mass interstices accompanied by coordinated electrical field reversals. This is to be done in such a way that *bipolar* cells will develop on each seed having long processes, extending in opposite directions, which resemble closely cerebral axons and dendrites. Furthermore, during subsequent operations of such a machine, it is expected that the size and shapes of these processes (especially gold *dendrites*) will change continually as a result of wave propagation through the aggregate and of externally applied massive shocks to be used during training sequences. Most work with dendrite growth has been done by submerging an anode and a cathode of an external power supply into a common reservoir of electrolyte. There was some question whether similar results could be obtained by induction on isolated metal seeds. This has now been accomplished using both gold and iron solutions. Figure 5 is an X-Ray picture of the first homogeneous aggregate in which such field-induced growth was actually observed. The large visible *chunks* are, in this case, small pieces of gold wire and close inspection reveals rudimentary dendritic growth on the end of each seed nearest the peripheral anode.

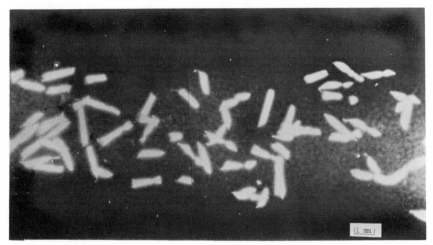

Figure 5. X-ray of metallic seeds and field-induced dendritic growths imbedded in glass aggregate.

WAVE PROPAGATION THROUGH POROUS CELL ASSEMBLIES

Following the series of preliminary stability tests described above, we wished to determine the possibility of stable wave propagation *through* a dense excitable aggregate. This demonstration was successfully carried out using several types of cell assemblies, containing as many as 600 iron cells. These cells or pellets were approximately 2 mm in diameter and were closely bonded together. In order to insure that the waves observed on the periphery of the cell cluster were, in fact, propagating *through* the cell asssembly rather than simply over its peripheral surface, the cell assembly was contained in an insulated box, one face of which was a glass plate which would allow visual observation. The cell assembly was excited in a variety of ways (both single and multiple point excitation) which resulted

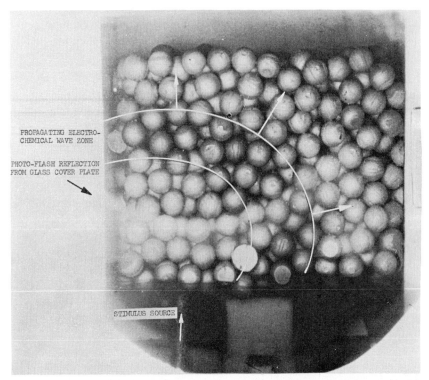

Figure 6. Electrochemical wave propagation through densely-packed porous aggregate of iron particles.

in a great variety of physical wave patterns. These wave patterns have been photographed in color on 16 mm motion picture film and the results are quite striking. Figure 6 clearly shows one such simple wave as it passes through the cell assembly. This particular wave was launched by exciting a small lead-in iron wire located just below the lower left-hand corner of the cell asssembly.

CONDITIONED RESPONSE MODEL

Several experiments have been conducted to study the critical coupling[3] parameters between two contiguous bipolar cells and to demonstrate reversible functional mutations induced by application of peripheral control fields. In these experiments the bipolar cells were essentially split so that a low impedance monitoring circuit could be used on the exterior of the test chamber to detect currents through the dipoles. In addition, for simplicity, the porous dielectric (glass) matrix in which we expect these cells to be imbedded in order to produce strong coupling was modelled by a simple solid dielectric barrier. The complete experimental assembly is shown in Fig. 7. In this photograph the gold dendritic ends of the cells

Figure 7. Conditioned response experimental assembly.

No coupling—21 ohms intercell impedance

Coupling—19 ohms intercell impedance

are imbedded in glass within the lower left circular cavity, the two iron cells may be seen in the lower right cavity, while the control electrode was located in the upper cavity. All these structures which are used in the high-pressure test chamber are *ventilated* to allow entry and circulation of liquid and pressure equalization between the inside and outside of the experimental assembly. In these experiments one of the cells (*primary*) was first stimulated by an external source while the circuit of the other cell (*secondary*) was opened to avoid artifact stimulation. Within 5 msec the original stimulus was removed and the external circuits of both cells were essentially closed. Two methods were then used to observe whether or not the *secondary* cell was induced to fire as a result of the excited state

of the primary cell: by visual observation of the surface of the secondary
cell and by recording the induced current through the secondary cell.
Figure 8 shows two photographs of a CRT display of the current through
the secondary cell under both *coupling* and *no coupling* conditions. The
change of intercell impedance required for this transition by growth or
diminution of the attached dendrites, as indicated on the figure, may be
seen to be quite small. The change recorded was sufficient to give a quasi-
stable change of function, i.e., very consistent performance (as determined
by several repeated tests) in the absence of further control shocks.

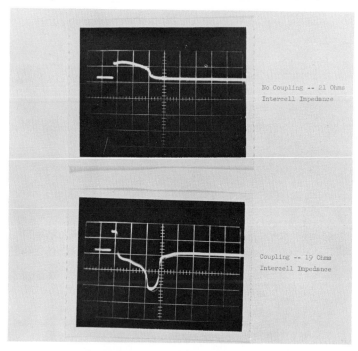

Figure 8. Induced current in secondary cell.

DIRECT STIMULATION BY LIGHT

Attempts to process exceedingly complex patterns of information with
a compact electrochemical integrative or logic unit would be seriously
handicapped or impossible if such parallel patterns of information had to
be introduced to the cellular assembly by means of electrical stimulation as
is now being done. For example, a parallel input system able to handle
million bit patterns (for example, 100×1000 picture elements) would
be unwieldy, to say the least, if it were necessary to have, say, one million

photo cells, one million amplifiers and one million stimulating probes. Ultimately, we hope to discover means of direct stimulation by incident ambient light much as in the retina of the eye. At present, this is not possible, but we have demonstrated that direct radiant stimulation is possible at somewhat higher light levels. In a rudimentary but convincing series of tests, it was demonstrated that a propagating wave could be triggered on an iron wire with a relatively low power pulsed ruby laser. The exact details of the mechanism are not yet known but further investigation should clarify this point. It was clear that focusing was critical, too small a spot being unable to propagate (as expected) and too large an illuminated area likewise failing to cause any breakdown at all of the oxide membrane due to insufficient energy density. In any case it should now be possible to construct an *image intensifier* consisting of a television camera whose scan pattern is synchronized with a light scanner and whose output intensity signals control modulation of the light source. This input will obviously not be exactly *parallel* but it should be possible to achieve approximately the same effect by an adequate choice of scanning and modulation rates.

STEREOTROPISM

In other experiments the growth of a dendrite toward an obstacle, especially an active metal cell, has been observed. The effect of such an obstacle on growth patterns is of interest for at least two reasons:

(a) Our analysis of intercellular coupling characteristics indicates that if such dendrites were to approach and finally fuse to an excitable cell body, the effect would essentially be to short-circuit or bypass the cell membrane, thus making an inhibitory coupling inoperative, and

(b) Possible modeling of the role of fields and obstacles in nerve fiber growth and synapse formation.

Although these results are all fragmentary at the present time, the primary effect of concern, i.e., failure to fuse, has been frequently observed. This result was not unexpected; it is probably caused by a mechanism involving local metallic ion depletion near the growing tip and the tendency to restrict replenishment by depletion as the gap between the dendrite and obstacle narrows.

SUMMARY AND CONCLUSIONS

During the past year progress has been made along a number of lines relating to the development of basic techniques for modelling and observing the behavior of complex electrochemical cell assemblies similar to those believed to be instrumental in brain functioning. A facility is now available which has eliminated violent instabilities through encapsulation and pressurization while at the same time increasing speed of response to rates comparable with those in the human nervous system. It has also been possible to demonstrate field induced growth of multiple dendrites imbedded in a porous dielectric matrix, to demonstrate stable wave propagation through dense porous cell assemblies, to demonstrate a simple reversible conditioned response in a three-cell system, to demonstrate direct excitation by incident light, and to demonstrate growth characteristics in dense cellular media leading to synaptic and ephaptic structures. Work currently in progress is aimed at further refinement and extension of these experimental investigations, at completely eliminating all formation of bubbles during all operations with various liquids contemplated, and at increasing complexity of excitable plastic systems under observation.

REFERENCES

1. R. M. Stewart, "Fields and Waves in Exitable Cellular Structures," *Proceedings First Pasadena Invitational Symposium on Self-Organizing Systems,* Office of Naval Research, Department of the Navy, Washington, D.C. Also to appear in Norbert Wiener Dedicatory Volume, v. 17, *Progress in Brain Research,* Elsevier, Amsterdam.

2. R. M. Stewart, "Learning Systems In and Out of the Factory," *1964 WESCON,* Los Angeles, California, Paper No. 3.4.

3. R. M. Stewart, "Adaptable Cellular Nets," *Progress in Biocybernetics,* v. 1, eds. Wiener and Schadé, Elsevier, Amsterdam, 1964, pp. 96-105.

ACKNOWLEDGMENT

The author wishes to acknowledge the invaluable advice and assistance of his associates in this work, Dr. J. R. Milne, Mr. George Hickey, and Mr. George Zombory.

4

APPLICATIONS OF A DIGITAL COMPUTER SIMULATION OF A NEURAL NETWORK*

DONALD H. PERKEL†

The RAND Corporation, Santa Monica, Calif.

THE ROLE OF NEURAL MODELING

The neuron model to be described has been developed as an adjunct to experimental neurophysiological investigations. The model and its applications, therefore, share a biological emphasis with the analog models of Harmon[1] and Lewis[2] and the digital computer simulations of Farley[3], as distinguished from the emphasis on bionics applications in the Perceptron[4], for example.

The intent of these neural modeling activities may be clarified through a scheme such as that of Fig. 1. The abscissa corresponds to relative complexity of a neural system, and the ordinate to the depth of our understanding of its operations, or to the predictive power of existing theories and models. Region A in this plane corresponds to mammalian central nervous systems: highly complex, with largely unknown operating principles. Region B corresponds to simpler biological nervous systems or

---

* This paper is based on research sponsored by the National Institutes of Health under Grant GM-09608-03. Much of the material presented has been reported in The RAND Corporation Memorandum RM-4132-NIH, June 1964, under the title *A Digital-Computer Model of Nerve Cell Functioning.*

† Any views expressed in this paper are those of the author. They should not be interpreted as reflecting the views of The RAND Corporation or the official opinion or policy of any of its governmental or private research sponsors.

37

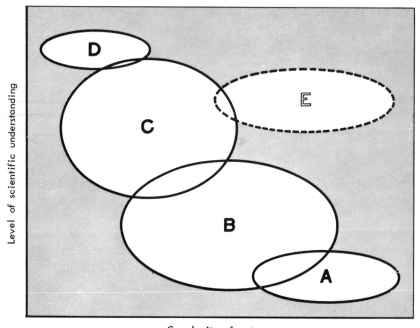

Figure 1. Understanding of neural systems.

parts thereof. Biologists study portions of peripheral nervous systems or relatively amenable and simple invertebrate preparations under the reasonable assumption that modes of neural functioning in simpler organisms persist, albeit in elaborated form and perhaps masked by other activity, in the more complex organisms.

Region D refers to the mathematical neuron models of the type devised by McCulloch and Pitts.[5] A high degree of abstraction from the properties of living nerve cells has enabled the construction of theorems and the development of a detailed theory of the behavoir of the neuron-like entities, but at the cost of so drastic a simplification of the properties of a neuron as to be at best of slight relevance to the neurophysiologist.

A major aim of the analog and digital nerve models mentioned, then, is to fill in the conceptual gap, represented by region C in Fig. 1. The mechanisms involved, electronic analog devices or digital computers, enable detailed and extended predictions to be made from much more complicated conceptual models than can be handled by "pencil-and-paper" techniques. The models can, in fact, be complex enough to serve as reasonably faithful simulations of portions of living nervous systems, so that parallel experiments can be performed on the model and on the system modeled.

By establishing such a continuity of overlapping regions in the plane, it is hoped ultimately to enhance our understanding of living nervous systems, so that regions A and B can eventually approach region E. This metaphor need not be belabored further, but it should be clear that for neural modeling to play its intended scientific role, there must be a continual interplay among the model maker, the model, and the "wet" experimenter.

DIGITAL AND ANALOG MODELS

The advantages of electronic analog models of neurons have been amply described and their usefulness has been convincingly demonstrated.[1, 2, 6] In our digital computer model of nerve cells and connecting fibers, it has been possible to retain many of these desirable features, e.g., a continuous rather than a coarsely quantized time scale, while taking advantage of properties peculiar to a digital simulation.[7] The inherent disdvantages of a digital computer model remain: these include its relative inaccessibility, the cumbersome way in which the model or the experiment is modified (i.e., through punched cards), and limitations of operating speed and storage capacity.

Several benefits ensue from the use of subroutines which generate pseudo-random numbers. The latter are reproducible sequences of numbers whose statistical properties are indistinguishable from those produced by a "truly random" sampling experiment. Such sequences are easily generated on a digital computer to represent sampling from uniform, normal, exponential, and gamma distributions. In a digital computer simulation of a number of neurons, *noise* or random fluctuations of specified properties may be introduced at literally any place in the system. The effects of various noise sources may thus be traced individually. Sampling distributions for complicated networks can be obtained simply by repeating the computations with different, but statistically equivalent, random sequences. On the other hand, an experiment may be repeated with the identical *noise* sequence using changed values of physiological parameters. Sources of variability are thus pinpointed from the start, obviating the necessity for performing an *a posteriori* analysis of variance.

A second major benefit of using the digital computer is related to statistical computations. Calculations of interspike interval distributions, auto- and cross-correlations, et cetera, may be performed while the primary data are available, in a suitable format, in the machine. Analog-to-digital conversion, which is required for statistical processing of experiments on living preparations or analog simulations, is thus avoided. The same programs, in fact, have been used for processing both experimental and simulated data.

Another incidental benefit of a digital simulation, if exploited, is the automatic recording of all the parameters and initial conditions of a run directly on the output listing, so that in effect the computer provides its own "laboratory" notebook.

THE PHYSIOLOGICAL MODEL

In our model, the neuron is composed of a soma and one or more fibers. The soma, strictly speaking, constitutes the spike-initiating locus of the cell, and postsynaptic phenomena are referred to their effects on that locus.

Two state variables are associated with the soma: the transmembrane potential and the threshold. Each of these variables undergoes a spontaneous drift, taken in the model as an exponential decay to its own asymptotic value, with its own decay constant. Synaptic events give rise to instantaneous *positive going* (excitatory or depolarizing) or *negative-going* (inhibitory or hyperpolarizing) shifts in the membrane potential, as illustrated in Fig. 2. When the potential attains or surpasses the cur-

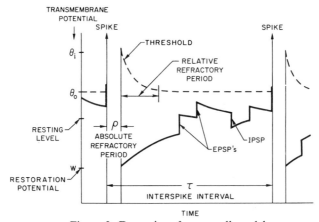

Figure 2. Dynamics of nerve-cell model.

rent threshold level, the cell fires, producing a spike, the time of whose occurrence is recorded by the program. Following a spike, the cell undergoes an absolute refractory period, at the end of which the potential and threshold are set to new values and continue their exponential drift.

At the moment of firing, an impulse starts to propagate along each of the fibers originating at a soma (axon collaterals are described as separate fibers). Upon arrival at the terminus of the fiber, the impulse causes the release of a quantity of "transmitter substance" at the synapse. The amount of transmitter may be constant (or drawn from a normal distribution) or may be a specified fraction of the current level of a reservoir. The depleted reservoir may be instantaneously augmented by a specified amount, after which it decays exponentially to an asymptotic level. By proper choice of parameters in the reservoir model, both facilitating and defacilitating temporal interactions may be introduced.

If the fiber terminates on a soma, the axosomatic synapse ordinarily [8] effects a positive or negative shift in membrane potential. This shift is proportional to the amount of transmitter substance released, and it may also depend upon the current value of the potential. Axo-axonic connections are also permitted, in which the reservoir level of the contacted fiber is increased or decreased.

If the asymptotic level of potential exceeds that of the threshold a "spontaneous" firing occurs at the time when the potential equals the threshold value. This results in a pacemaker action; the regularity of firings is modified by the synaptic input received by the pacemaker cell.

Nearly all of the physiological parameters mentioned—conduction time along a fiber, initial and asymptotic values of state variables, decay constants, absolute refractory periods, etc.—may be fixed or drawn at random from a normal, exponential, or gamma distribution with specified parameters.

In addition to somas and fibers, the model includes external sources of impulses, which may be thought of as arising from other cells or from an external stimulator. Impulses produced by any such sources may occur regularly, according to a recurring schedule, at normally distributed intervals, or according to a Poisson or integral-order Erlang process.

Fibers may connect sources or somas to fibers or somas in a nearly unrestricted variety, so that complicated networks may be built up, ad libitum, involving feedback loops of any degree of complexity. In particular, a fiber may synapse on its own cell body, simulating a recurrent collateral.

THE COMPUTER PROGRAM

The computer program that embodies this model is written almost entirely in Fortran IV (the single exception being the uniform random-number generator).[9]

The program has the capacity for 350 components; the partitioning among sources, somas, and fibers is specified in the input data. The net structure is thus extremely flexible; the interconnections may be as dense or sparse as desired, within the overall size limitation.

The program does not utilize constant time increments, but rather jumps from each "interesting event" to the next. The types of interesting events are as follows: the production of an impulse by a source, the emergence of a soma from its absolute refractory period, the spontaneous firing of a soma, the arrival of an impulse at the terminus of fiber, and the extrinsic imposition of a parameter change. At each interesting event, the necessary state variables are updated to the current clock time, the effects of the event are computed and recorded appropriately, and any new interesting times that are a direct consequence of the current event are predicted and recorded. For example, if the event is the arrival of an impulse at an axosomatic synapse, the next arriving impulse (if any) along the fiber is set as the next interesting time for the fiber, the reservoir contents of the synapse are brought up to date, the quantity of transmitter substance to be released is computed, the threshold and potential of the postsynaptic cell are brought up to date, the updated potential is augmented or diminished by the magnitude of the postsynaptic potential according to the specified combining rule, and the cell is tested for firing. If it does not fire, it is tested for future spontaneous firing (possible with certain combinations of parameters and state variables). If the cell does fire, the time of its emergence from the refractory period is computed and the arrival times of impulses in all efferent fibers are predicted and stored. A condensed flow diagram of the program is shown in Fig. 3.

Through the use of special list-processing techniques, the program keeps track of "piled-up" impulses in transit along any fiber. The number of impulses that may be simultaneously in transit along any fiber is arbitrary, subject only to a limitation on the total number of such piled-up impulses in existence at any one time.

OUTPUT STATISTICS AND DATA PROCESSING

The output of the program consists almost entirely of data concerning the spikes produced, i.e., the times of occurrence of neuron firings. *Spike-train* statistics are computed for each cell indivdually, and pairwise comparisons are made between cells.

Identical computer subroutines are used to process suitably digitized experimental spike train data as are used for processing the computer-simulated data. Interval sequences or *spike times* are printed on line and

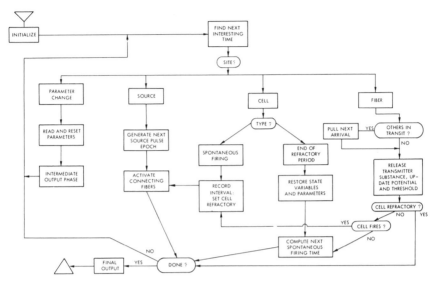

Figure 3. Network simulation program.

can also be put on magnetic tape or punched cards for later processing or special computations. Scalar quantities characterizing the spike trains from each cell include: the mean interspike interval; its standard deviation, variance, and coefficient of variation; second, third, and fourth moments about the interval mean; measures of skewness and kurtosis; mean firing rate; and ratio of number of spikes to input pulses. Serial correlation coefficients of the sequence of intervals are computed up to any specified order.

Histograms of observed interspike interval distributions are printed (and plotted on-line) up to any order. ⸱ (An n'th-order interval is the interval between n successive spikes.) The sum of the interspike interval distributions for all orders, known as autocorrelation [10] or expectation density,[11] is also computed; it represents the probability per unit time of encountering a spike as a function of the time subsequent to an actual spike. The joint interval distribution [10] is printed as a matrix representing a two-dimensional histogram. Matrix element (i, j) represents the number of occurrences of an interval in range j followed by an interval in range i. The matrix is also normalized so that its elements represent transition probabilities from one interval range to another in a hypothetical Markov chain. Row and column means are furnished as an indicator of serial dependence.[10]

Comparison of two simultaneous spike trains is made through the cross-correlation histogram [12], which measures the probability per unit time of encountering a spike in train B as a function of time before or after the actual occurrence of a spike in record A. A peak in the cross-correlation histogram (e.g., Fig. 4) may indicate a "preferred" firing interval between

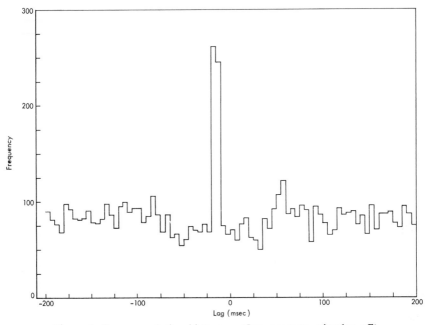

Figure 4. Cross-correlation histogram (Interneurons, stimulus off).

the two cells, such as might be caused by one cell exciting another, or by shared excitatory input.[13] A variation of this measure is the cross-phase histogram, in which the latencies from the A spike to the B spike are normalized with respect to the adjacent interval in A; the cross-phase histogram is computed using Wilson's method.[14]

On option, the program can also keep track of the fluctuations of membrane potential in designated cells, and produce mean and fractional *stay-time* histograms of the membrane potential, transition probabilities per unit time between intervals of membrane potential, and related quantities.

An output phase can be produced for any specified time segments of a simulation run, as well as for the entire run. Typically, an intermediate output is furnished for each time interval between parameter changes, but other variations are permitted.

As a byproduct of the computer model, various types of numerical data on magnetic tape can be converted by machine into suitable form for automatic plotting by use of a cathode ray tube. We have utilized this capability to plot histograms, using the Stromberg-Carlson SC-4020 machine, and have obtained reproducible page-size plots as well as 35-mm film strips for mounting and projection as slides.

A more novel application of the automatic plotting capabilities is the production of animated motion-picture displays of ongoing activity in a neural net. Locations of sources and somas in a plane are furnished to the computer, as well as pathways for the fibers, which are broken into connected straight-line segments. From these data, and with the firing times of sources and somas already stored on tape, the computer reconstructs, frame by frame, a series of "snapshots" of the activity. Impulses in transit along fibers are represented by small spots of light, and the firing of a soma is represented by an expanding and then contracting disk of light. The series of frames is produced on a continuous strip of film, which is then projected with an ordinary movie projector. The resulting motion picture is a partial realization of Sherrington's vision of the "enchanted loom." [15]

MODIFICATIONS TO THE MODEL

Within the framework of the network simulation program, changes in various features of the model may be made with comparative ease. The simplest changes are those that can be expressed through changes in numerical parameters, which are part of the input data for a given run. For example, a given synapse may embody a facilitatory or a defacilitatory mode of temporal interaction among arriving impulses, by a simple input change.

In another example, program changes (easily fitted in with Fortran) were required. In order to permit a type of "fatigue" mechanism not arising from the earlier model, the asymptotic threshold level was changed from a parameter to a state variable (on option). The asymptotic level decays exponentially to a "basal" level; when, however, an impulse arrives at the appropriate type of synapse (used so far only for recurrent collaterals), the asymptotic level is augmented by a specified amount. In this way, a cell producing a burst of spikes can undergo "fatigue" which renders it relatively inexcitable, by an exponentially decreasing amount.

A third example has not yet been incorporated into the overall network scheme, but has been tested by a separate program. Instead of the unrealistic step changes that represent postsynaptic potentials, the modification uses the difference of two exponential functions to produce the much more realistic "wave forms" shown in Fig. 5. The non-commutativity of spatial summation is illustrated in the third line of record, where afferent impulses 2 and 5 produce a different maximum depolarization from that produced by 5 followed by 2.

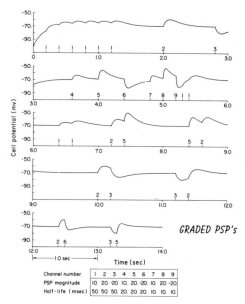

Figure 5. Graded PSPs.

APPLICATIONS OF THE MODEL

PACEMAKER INTERACTIONS

An early application of the model elucidated patterns of activity undergone by two pacemaker cells, one of which makes an inhibitory or excitatory synaptic connection with another. Details of these studies have been presented elsewhere [16, 17]. The computer simulations predicted the results of an experiment that had already been performed independently (on crayfish stretch receptor neurons, Ref. 17), but which had not yet reached the acquaintance of the "computer experimenters." Some types of patterned activity were predicted by the computer and subsequently found in old intracellular records from visceral ganglion neurons of sea slug. Some of these effects involved a "paradoxical" increase in firing rate of a neuron when the rate if *inhibitory* input was increased. This occurred in well defined ranges of mean input rate. The computer simulations were able to show how this sharply defined *input-output* relationship "washed away" as the input pacemaker was allowed to become more and more irregular; this was a kind of experiment difficult or impossible to perform in the living preparation.

The original results have been extended to a *tree* of monosynaptically inhibiting pacemakers, with no feedback or reciprocal innervation. The twenty neurons exhibited a regular, steady sequence of firing, which was disrupted by either (a) disconnecting the apical pacemaker, or (b) introducing impulses from Poisson noise sources to various cells of the tree. Upon cessation of the disrupting condition, the cells spontaneously re-established their original firing pattern, during a period corresponding to approximately eight firing cycles.

A MECHANISM OF BURST.FORMATION

If two pacemaker cells of similar but not identical frequencies supply input to a common "target," the latter will observe clusters of near coincidences of impulses at the beat frequency (the difference between the two pacemaker frequencies). If the target consists of a neuron whose threshold is slightly less than two EPSP amplitudes more positive than the resting level of potential, that cell will fire only when these near coincidences are received. The resultant firing pattern of the target cell will consist of bursts of spikes, with the bursts occurring at the beat frequency. This is shown in the first record of Fig. 6.

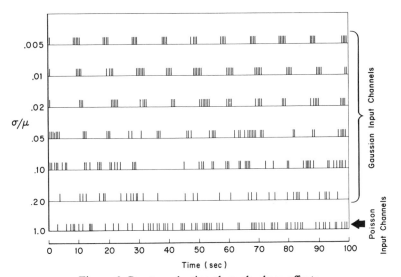

Figure 6. Burst production through phase effects.

This result could have been obtained through pencil-and-paper methods; the extensions of it, however, illustrate the power of the computer model. If we keep the mean interspike intervals of the pacemakers constant, but allow the variance of the intervals (drawn from a Gaussian distribution) to increase, we observe at first a minor deterioration in the uniformity of the bursts. As the coefficient of variation reaches five and ten percent, however, we observe an extremely erratic firing sequence which appears much more chaotic than for cases with even greater input variance: Gaussian with 20% standard deviation and Poisson channels (coefficient of variation of unity).

SAMPLING OF MEMBRANE POTENTIAL

It has been pointed out by Moore [18] that information can be stored in a "silent" cell in the distribution of its transmembrane potential. This distribution has been measured in simulated neurons as well as in sea slug visceral ganglion neurons. Both the mean and the shape of the temporal distribution of potential change with input intensity, sign (i.e., inhibitory or excitory), arrival rate, and degree of uniformity of arrival intervals. If a "test" neuron "queries" such a cell by sending a single EPSP (or a short burst), then the ordinarily silent cell will fire with a certain probability, depending upon the membrane potential distribution, threshold value, and magnitude of test EPSP. A bank of such cells in parallel can supply sufficient redundancy for relatively precise measurement or hypothesis testing. In order to do this the output fibers from the silent cells converge on an integrating cell, which requires a near coincidence of some small number of impulses to fire. The integrating cell thus fires only when the test cell evokes responses from some minimal number of the silent cells; this firing constitutes a *yes* answer to the inquiry.

In addition to this "response" mode of action, the system has an automatic "emergency override" action. If the input intensity or rate to the silent cells becomes sufficiently great, the silent cells will fire even when not subjected to the test EPSP's. If a sufficient number of such non-test firings occur, the integrating cell will fire in the absence of inquiry. An additional delayed-coincidence circuit between the test cell and the integrating cell can separate the *yes* responses from the override signal. Moore and Segundo [19] have pointed out possible physiological examples of such systems.

SEMI-EMPIRICAL CONFIDENCE INTERVALS

As a final example of the applications of the neural network simulator, we consider the generation of confidence limits on statistical measures by the performance of replicate runs on the computer, using different sequences of random numbers. Various properties of nerve cells, such as adaptation, fatigue, delayed interaction among various state variables, and interaction effects, tend to confer upon successive observations of cells, for example—intervals between firings—a degree of dependence. This often undermines the assumption of independent trials which underlies the basis of many statistical tests. Both the lack of independence and the complicated nature of some statistical measurements (e.g., the *cross-phase* histograms) render it difficult or impossible to construct rigorous mathematical formulations of confidence intervals for statistical measurements on spike trains (e.g., Ref. 20).

By repeating a simulation run under identical conditions but different realizations of the stochastic processes involved, i.e., using different sequences of random numbers, confidence limits for cross- and autocorrelations and other measures can be obtained empirically. Such techniques have been used, for example, in the analysis of experiments in which the responses of cells to nearly Poisson-source input (i.e., Geiger-counter output) have been analyzed [21].

In a similar way, the simulations can be used to obtain rules of thumb for the required duration of experiments in which possible interactions are to be detected. The duration depends, of course, upon the maximum tolerable probabilities of both kinds of errors: false attribution of interaction, or failure to detect real interaction.

EFFECTIVE EXPLOITATION OF NERVE MODELS

The neural network simulation program has been in use in approximately its present form for little more than a year. Although it has been of considerable use both in the interpretation of experiments and in the development of statistical measures of spike activity, its real usefulness has not yet begun to be exploited.

For example, the maximum number of nerve cells simulated in a network has been about two dozen, whereas the program is capable of simulating well over a hundred cells and their associated fibers. Simulation of specific neural pathways of living nervous systems has been confined to at most four or five cells. Furthermore, the flexibility of physiological description of neurons has been very lightly tapped.

The present limitations of the model in terms of realism and size do not in fact represent limitations on its effective use. A challenge is made to neurophysiologists to seek appropriate applications. Imaginative, consistent use of a model of this sort, in conjunction with and as a complement to experimental investigations, can lead to closing of the conceptual gap of Fig. 1; only this will constitute effective exploitation of these new tools.

REFERENCES

1. L. D. Harmon, "Artificial Neuron," *Science 129,* 962-963, 1959.
2. E. R. Lewis, "An Electronic Analog of the Neuron Based on the Dynamics of Potassium and Sodium Fluxes," *Neural Theory and Modeling,* R. F. Reiss, Ed., Stanford Univ. Press, Palo Alto, Cal., 1964.
3. B. G. Farley and W. A. Clark, "Activity in Networks of Neuron-Like Elements," *Proceedings Fourth London Symposium on Information Theory,* Butterworths, London, 1961.
4. F. Roseblatt, *Principles of Neurodynamics: Perceptrons and the Theory of Brain Mechanisms,* Spartan Books, Washington, D. C., 1962.
5. W. S. McCulloch and W. Pitts, "A Logical Calculus of the Ideas Immanent in Nervous Activity," *Bull. Math. Biophysics 5,* 115-133, 1943.
6. L. D. Harmon, "Neuromimes: Action of a Reciprocally Inhibitory Pair," *Science 146,* 1323-1325, 1964.
7. D. H. Perkel, *A Digital-Computer Model of Nerve-Cell Functioning,* The RAND Corporation, Memorandum RM-4132-NIH, June 1964.
8. Special synapses may affect the asymptotic level.
9. The program operates at RAND on the IBM 7044 computer. A 7094 version has been placed into operation at the University of California at Los Angeles and at the California Institute of Technology.
10. R. W. Rodieck, S. Kiang, and G. L. Gerstein, "Some Quantitative Methods for the Study of Spontaneous Activity of Single Neurons," *Biophysical Jour. 4,* 351-368, 1962.
11. G. F. Poggio and L. J. Viernstein, "Time Series Analysis of Impulse Sequences of Thalamic Somatic Sensory Neurons," *Jour Neurophysiol. 27,* 517-545, 1964.
12. G. L. Gerstein and N. Y.-S. Kiang, "An Approach to the Quantitative Analysis of Electrophysiological Data from Single Neurons," *Biophysical Jour. 1,* 15-28, 1960.
13. D. H. Perkel, *Direction of Functional Interactions Among Neurons: A Technique Using Repetitive Presentations of Stimuli,* The RAND Corporation, Memorandum RM-4234-NIH, August 1964.
14. D. M. Wilson and R. J. Wyman, "Motor Output Patterns During Random and Rhythmic Stimulation of Locust Thoracic Ganglia," *Biophysical Jour.,* in press.

15. C. Sherrington, *Man on his Nature,* 2nd edit., Cambridge Univ. Press, Cambridge, 1953; pp. 176-178, *passim.* An example of such a film was shown at the Symposium.

16. G. P. Moore, J. P. Segundo, and D. H. Perkel, "Stability Patterns in Interneuronal Pacemaker Regulation," *Proceedings of the San Diego Symposium for Biomedical Engineering,* A. Paull, Ed. (San Diego Symposium for Biomedical Engineering, La Jolla, Calif., 1963); pp. 184-193.

17. D. H. Perkel, J. H. Schulman, T. H. Bullock, G. P. Moore, and J. P Segundo, "Pacemaker Neurons: Effects of Regularly Spaced Synaptic Input," *Science 145,* 61-63, 1964.

18. G. P. Moore, "Some Neuronal Functions which are Equivalent to Information Storage and Retrieval," *Symposium on Coding of Information in the Nervous System,* American Electroencephalographic Society, 18th Annual Meeting, Santa Fe, New Mexico, October 1964.

19. G. P. Moore, J. P. Segundo, and D. H. Perkel, "Post-synaptic Membrane Potential Distribution as a Representation of Input State," *Physiologist 7,* 209, 1964. A 10-cell bank of such cells, with mixed excitatory and inhibitory input, was the subject of the film presented at the Symposium (See reference 15).

20. J. S. Griffith and G. Horn, "Functional Coupling Between Cells in the Visual Cortex of the Unrestrained Cat," *Nature 199,* 876-895, 1963.

21. J. P. Segundo, G. P. Moore, and D. H. Perkel, "Spike Probability in *Aplysia* Neurons as a Function of the Number, Span and Timing of Recent Input Events," in preparation.

5

BIOLOGICAL PROCESSING OF VISUAL INFORMATION

J. A. DALY*, M. UEMURA*, S. S. VIGLIONE*,
R. L. BINGGELLI† and H. F. WOLF‡

INTRODUCTION

This paper reports the results of some recent electronic modeling experiments, performed to gain insights about the neuronal data processing capabilities of the vertebrate retina. It is felt that the large size and complex interactions of neural systems in general require mechanistic aids for their study. The approach of electronic modeling was chosen because it provides a simple framework in which theories of neural operation may be derived, and an immediate means of exploration and verification of the ramifications of these theories.

It was decided that the pigeon retina would be the immediate object to be modeled. This decision was based primarily on the availability of pertinent physiological and anatomical data. The pigeon has the further advantages for study in that the eye is somewhat similar to that of man, with a single fovea, color vision, and about one million fibers in the optic nerve.[1] Finally, the pigeon is phylogenetically between other animals for which models of visual processes have been constructed,[2] thus fitting into a continuum of models.

*Astropower Laboratory, Missile & Space Systems Division, Douglas Aircraft Company, Inc., Newport Beach, Calif.
†University of Southern California, School of Medicine, Los Angeles, Calif.
‡Aeronutronic Division of Philco Corporation, Newport Beach, Calif.

The principal innovations of the current program appear to be in the electronic modeling devices. The neuron models of the current system have temporal characteristics similar to real neurons. Further, they are incorporated in a device which allows rapid interconnection of elements.

SUMMARY OF ANATOMICAL AND PHYSIOLOGICAL DATA

The avian retina is a layered structure as is schematically shown in Fig. 1. The receptor cells transform incoming light signals to electrochemical

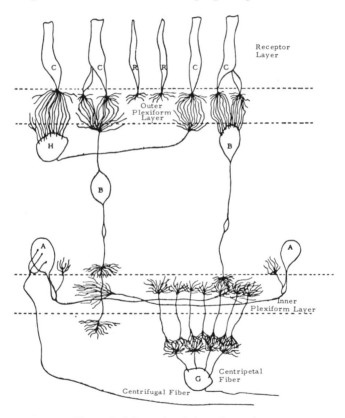

Figure 1. Schematic of the avian retina.

signals. (In the model the outputs at this layer are assumed to be slow varying d. c. rather than pulses.) Both rod, (R) and cone (C) receptors are found in the pigeon, but cones predominate. The receptor outputs occur in the outer plexiform layer, which also contains arborizations of horizontal (H) and bipolar (B) cells.

Bipolar cells conduct information from the outer to the inner plexiform layer. They thus form the first link in the transmission chain from the receptors to the brain. The response of the bipolar cell is a spike response.[3]

Horizontal cells are internuncials, with both input and output arborizations in the outer plexiform layer. In the current model it is assumed that these cells provide the spike potentials noted in this layer.[4] A second class of internuncial cells are the amacrines (A), which appear to have input and output arborizations in the inner plexiform layer. Amacrine cells also have synaptic inputs from centrifugal fibers from the brain.[5]

The third major class of cells with arborizations in the inner plexiform layer are the ganglion cells (G). The axons of the ganglion cells form the optic nerve. Tables 1 and 2 summarize the anatomical considerations used in this study to model the selected portions of the pigeon retina.

TABLE 1

Approximate* Dimensions of Components of the Avian Retina

Cell Type	Diameter	Length	Spread of Input	Arborization Output	Density
Cones	4μ	6μ	. . .	$12\text{-}20\mu$	$17/40\mu$ in 2 layers
Horizontals	6μ	$60\text{-}80\mu$	$12\text{-}20\mu$	$12\text{-}20\mu$	$74/40\mu$
Bipolars	4μ	. . .	$12\text{-}20\mu$	$12\text{-}20\mu$	in 8 layers
Amacrines	. . .	$60\text{-}120\mu$	small	100μ	$40/40\mu$ in 5 layers
Ganglions	8μ	. . .	100μ	. . .	$9/40\mu$ in 2 layers

* Densities are taken from Chievitz [6] for the pigeon retina periphery 3mm from the area centralis. Other dimensions are gathered from a variety of sources.

The output of the ganglion cells are spike potentials. Recent microelectrode studies in several animals have indicated that the information represented by these spike potentials to the brain is a rather sophisticated extraction of pattern features of the light stimulus. Recordings made in the optic tectum of the pigeon by Wylie[1] indicated cells with several classes of receptive fields. Some of these seem sufficiently simple that they may represent recordings from the axons of retinal ganglion cells. Typically these simple cells had two receptive fields with different modes of response; the fields were concentric, of different size, and mutually antagonistic in response. The inner fields usually had an *ON-OFF* response to an

TABLE 2

Approximate Number of Cells in a 40 Minute Area of the Pigeon Retina
(in the periphery 3mm from the area centralis)

Cell Type	Number of Cells
Cones	450
Horizontals & Bipolars	2000
Amacrines	1000
Ganglions	130
Centrifugally Controlled Amacrines	1

illuminating spot of light. That is, the ganglion responded with a short burst of pulses to both the onset and cessation of stimulating illumination. The outer fields had either an *ON* response or an *OFF* response, but usually required an anulus of light as stimulus to evoke this response. The inner receptive fields of these cells were from one to five degrees in extent, and the outer annuli were one to two degrees in width.

Most of these cells responded vigorously to a moving spot, independent of the direction of motion within the field. The exception was one recorded cell with an *OFF* outer receptive field, which responded to a moving spot only when the spot centripetally traversed the boundary between the cell's receptive fields.

In contrast to these cells, Maturana and Frenk[7] have reported *directional movement detector* ganglion cells, each of which responds preferentially to stimuli moving in a specific direction. These cells are reported to have a single receptive field, one half to one degree in diameter, which has an *ON-OFF* response to stationary stimulus. They respond with strings of spike potentials to a stimulus moving in the correct direction, independent of the shape of the stimulus, and independent of whether it is lighter or darker than the background. Two stimuli, moving in opposite directions, do not elicit a response.

A second class of ganglion cells reported by Maturana and Frenk are the *horizontal edge detectors*. These cells do not respond at all to the *ON* or *OFF* of a spot of light. They respond maximally to up or down motion of a horizontal edge across the receptive field, with the edge extending beyond the boundaries of the field. The field size is 20 to 40 minutes of arc.

THE ELECTRONIC MODELING DEVICE

The basic elements of the electronic model are the analogs of the actual transmission cells of the retina: cones, bipolars and ganglions. The functioning of these analog cells is described with reference to Fig. 2.

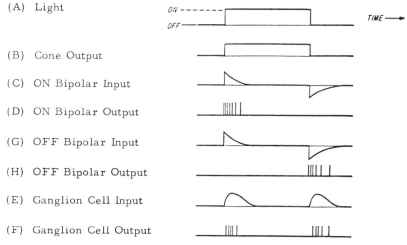

Figure 2. Basic waveforms of the electronic modeling system.

The cones are modeled as providing a step voltage, porportional in amplitude and equal in duration to the input light stimulus. Physically the cone analog consists of a photodiode and an emitter follower. The cone analogs are individually adjusted by means of load resistors to have equivalent response characteristics. The output circuits have *fan-out* capacity to provide ten bipolar inputs.

Four bipolar models have been designed, corresponding to four different categories of possible bipolar responses. All of these are based on a circuit described by Harmon[8], and shown in Fig. 3. The categories of bipolars are specified by two parameters: (a) continuing or burst responses, and (b) *ON* or *OFF* responses. The bipolar responses shown in Fig. 2. are both of the burst type. The *ON* response is a response to the onset of stimulus. The *OFF* response is to cessation of stimulus.

The basic Harmon neuron of Fig. 3. has five excitatory inputs and one inhibitory input, shown to the left of the diagram. (In the current circuits, five inhibitory inputs are used.) The excitatory inputs contribute current which is accumulated in the capacitor, C_1, providing temporal summation of the input voltages. When the voltage across C_1 reaches a

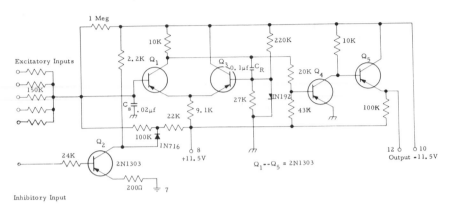

Figure 3. Harmon neuron.

threshold, the monostable multivibrator circuit involving T_1 and T_3 produces a pulse. The pulse is amplified by T_4 and T_5 before it is transmitted to the output lead. Capacitor C_2 acts as a storage device for the refractory recovery phenomenon, setting the threshold for the pulse generator circuit. Transistor T_2 controls the inhibition, by controlling the voltage level on the base of transistor T_1 through a zener diode.

The circuit described is essentially the *ON,* continuous bipolar model. The circuit modifications used to transform the model to an *OFF* or burst model are minor. The *OFF* circuit has a one transistor inverter inserted between T_1 and the excitatory resistor-summing network. The burst response circuit has a capacitor inserted in the same location. An *OFF,* burst-response bipolar circuit is shown in Fig. 4. It may be noted that it is constructed on a vectorboard, to allow further modification as required.*

The ganglion circuit is essentially the same as the bipolar circuit, but has a greater available *fan-in.*

While it is quite possible to utilize the neuron models which have been discussed as horizontal and amacrine analogs, this has not been done in the current work. It has been assumed that these internuncial cells do not perform logic with respect to their inputs, but merely transmit local signal averages from one point of the retina to another, within the same plexiform layer. Moreover, it has been assumed in these preliminary experiments that such connections are always inhibitory. For these reasons, horizontals (or

---

* The smaller circuit is a less expensive, higher speed circuit, designed at Astropower, with similar capabilities. However, its higher frequency of response does not lend itself to the current program.

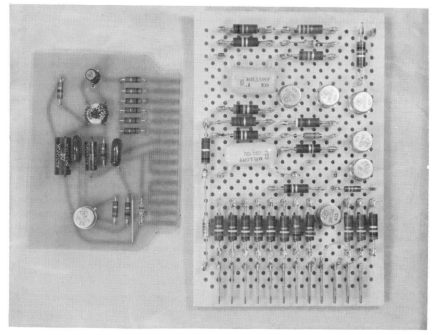

Figure 4. Analog neuron circuit cards.

amacrines) have been modeled as connections from cones (or bipolars) to the inhibitory inputs of bipolars (or ganglions).

The actual modeling device is shown in Fig. 5. The photodiodes representing the cones are mounted in the plane shown in the left foreground. Pattern stimuli are applied to this area by masking the illumination from the floodlight mounted above the plane. The cone amplifiers and neuron models are mounted in the chassis on the right of the picture. Connections of the outer plexiform layer are represented by connections in the top plugboard. The bottom plugboard represents the inner plexiform layer. The speakers and oscilloscope are the output devices for the system.

The system as it is shown contains 80 cone analogs, 72 bipolar analogs and 8 ganglion analogs. Work is underway to substantially increase its size.

NEURAL SYSTEM MODELS

Utilizing this system, several hypothetical neural system models have been investigated. The following are some of the more interesting findings.

It has been noted that the natural response of the "Harmon neuron" to a d.c. input is a periodic sequence of pulses. A system has been con-

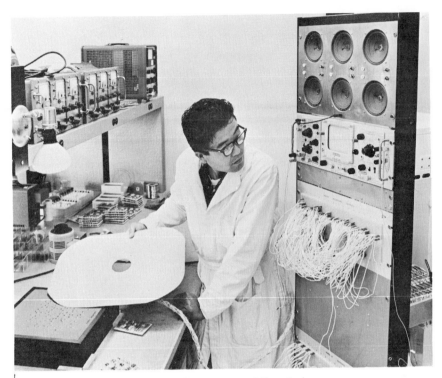

Figure 5. Pigeon eye modeling device.

structed consisting of (a) a cone analog, providing continuous voltage output proportional to the stimulus light, (b) a bipolar analog which trans-
forms the signal to the pulse frequency code, and (c) a ganglion analog
which relays the signal to the display device. Over a wide amplitude range
the frequency of pulses shows a logarithmic dependence on the input
amplitude similar to that encountered in psychophysical measurements.

By use of *ON* and *OFF* bipolar cells, a system has been constructed
which shows the *ON-OFF* behavior typical of the inner receptive field of
the cells reported by Wylie.[1] The simplest such system consists of two cone
analogs, an *ON* bipolar analog, an *OFF* bipolar analog, and a ganglion
analog. It responds to the onset and termination of illumination with a
short burst of pulses.

A horizontal edge detection system has also been constructed. The network consists of a number of bipolar analogs, each of which responds
uniquely to a horizontal edge in one position on the receptive field. The
response is based on excitatory and inhibitory inputs from cone analogs

in the vicinity of this unique edge position. A ganglion analog is connected to respond whenever any of these bipolar analogs responds. Therefore the ganglion analog responds for any of a wide variety of horizontal edge stimuli within the receptive field.

A moving spot detector system has also been constructed, consisting of a large number of *ON* and *OFF* bipolar analogs and a ganglion analog which responds if any of the bipolars energize it. The bipolars have circular receptive fields, which overlap, and respond only to a change of illumination. A moving spot evokes responses in some cells by moving into their receptive fields and evokes responses from others by moving out of their receptive field. The ganglion continues to respond as long as any of its input bipolars respond, i.e., as long as the spot moves in its larger receptive field.

Finally, a system has been constructed that responds to a moving edge, with a response which depends strongly on the direction of motion. This system depends on a number of bipolar analogs which tend to inhibit a ganglion analog response, and which have receptive fields distributed fairly regularly over the receptor plane. A smaller number of bipolar analogs are connected to excite the ganglion cell and their individual receptive fields are clustered in one area, toward the edge of the receptor plane. An edge which preferentially illuminates the excitatory bipolar analogs elicits a response from the ganglion analog. This occurs if a light edge moves toward the center of the receptor plane through this excitatory area. Thus there is a preferential directional response.

DISCUSSION

The results reported in this paper are preliminary, and represent the initial experience with the modeling device. This experience has indicated that the electronic system is a convenient and useful tool in the formulation and exploration of theoretical models of retinal function. The initial experience has also indicated that the functions already recorded for retinal ganglion cells are extremely complex in terms of the available logical depth. While it seems possible to rapidly find systems capable of the required responses, these easily derived systems seem intuitively undesirable in that they require more connectional specificity than is usually granted possible in neural systems. Little success has been achieved in finding broad statistical connection specifications that reproduce the complex functional networks reported by Maturana and Frenk. It is hoped that these problems will be partially resolved through more effective utilization of the temporal properties of these neuron analogs.

REFERENCES

1. R. M. Wylie, "Response of Neurons in the Optic Tectum of the Pigeon," Ph.D. Thesis, Harvard University, Cambridge, Mass., April 1962.

2. M. B. Herrscher, and T. P. Kelley, "Functional Electronic Model of the Frog Retina," *IEEE Transactions on Military Electronics,* Vol. MIL-7, April-July 1963, pp 98-103 and personal communications from F. Rosenblatt respecting computer modeling of visual processes in the cat.

3. Brown and Weisel, quoted on p 123, H. Davson, *The Physiology of the Eye,* Little, Brown and Company, Boston, 2nd Edition, 1963.

4. K. Motokawa, "Mechanisms for the Transfer of Information Along the Visual Pathways," *International Review of Neurobiology,* Vol. 5, Academic Press, New York, 1963.

5. W. M. Cowan, and T. P. S. Powell, "Centrifugal Fibers in the Avian Visual System," *Royal Society Proceedings,* Ser. B, Vol. 158, 1963, pp 232-252.

6. J. H. Chievitz, "Untersuchungen ueber die Apea Centralis Retinae," *Arch. Anat. Entwicklungsgesch,* Suppl. 139, 1889, pp 139-196.

7. H. R. Maturana, and S. Frenk, "Directional Movement and Horizontal Edge Detectors in the Pigeon Retina," *Science,* Vol. 142, 15 Nov. 1963, pp 977-979.

8. L. D. Harmon, and J. Levinson, "Analog Model of Neural Mechanisms," *IRE Transactions on Information Theory,* Feb. 1962.

6

CENTRAL NERVOUS SYSTEM SYMMETRY
AND SPATIAL DISCRIMINATION

R. L. BINGGELI
University of Southern California at Los Angeles
School of Medicine

The topic of the symmetrical organization of the central nervous system is perhaps at the opposite end of the spectrum from the subject matter of most of the papers presented at this, the Second Cybernetic Sciences Symposium. They have been involved with elementary properties of logical operations and of the fine details of neuron or neuron-like structure and function. I, instead, would like to discuss some of the possible relations between some aspects of the overall external form of the nervous system, its basic layout, and some of its functions.

A casual conceptualization of the basic scheme of the nervous system usually includes the basic *input-output* aspects, the sensory and motor divisions. A more sophisticated concept might involve a hierarchical arrangement of brain parts, from *lower* to *higher* centers through which the massive input from sensory transducers is filtered, involving a gradual information loss according to preset rules (which are capable of being modified, i.e. learning). This superficial approach does not, however, take into account one of the most basic attributes of the nervous system, bilateral symmetry, which is essentially a duplication of the entire pattern of the nervous system on each side of the organism. This duplication does not fit any of our intuitive ideas on how we would build a nervous system. For why do we and most other land animals have what amounts to two brains?

63

A simple reason could be redundancy, protection against loss by having two parallel, essentially equivalent, systems. This has certainly been borne out both experimentally and clinically with clear demonstrations of the great plasticity of the brain in recovering function after unilateral damage. But surely this cannot be the only reason that such an exquisitely architectural structure is doubled. (It may be asked why other vital organs such as the heart and liver are not duplicated, but this may lead to a teleological argument.)

Only recently have there been many serious attempts to discover the functional relationship between symmetrical brain parts. Sperry[1] and others have been attempting to elucidate the nature of the transfer of information between the two halves of the forebrain, primarily through separating the halves (the "split-brain" preparation) and testing for functional loss. This procedure has delineated the necessity of the connections between symmetrical parts for the sharing of experiences between them.

J. Z. Young[2] and S. Ramon y Cajal have suggested that bilateral symmetry may be related to the problem of dealing with two images coming from the two eyes necessary for binocular vision and/or for wide field perception. But it seems unlikely that the visual system would dictate the entire organization of the central nervous system, especially since bilateral symmetry was well established long before the development of visual organs in the evolutionary picture.

This brings up the question of the origin of bilateral symmetry in the long history of animal development. Is this a structural design which has come about through acquisition of an axis of symmetry from a basically asymmetrical condition? Or is this rather not the last vestige from what was primitively a totally symmetrical organism? At every level in the animal kingdom there are representatives whose basic structural organization is totally asymmetrical. This argues against the latter alternative. It can be countered, however, that all modern animals, no matter how lowly their position phylogenetically, are advanced developments *within* groups and that there are few true examples of primitive states now living. Speaking for the alternative that present bilateral symmetry is a vestigial, indeed even disappearing condition is a vast group of clinical neurologists, in particular H. L. Teuber,[3] who have demonstrated relatively uniquely in humans a fundamental asymmetry within the grossly appearing bilateral symmetry. Many functions become selectively positioned in one half of the cerebrum (the center controlling speech is usually located in the left hemisphere). In the higher mammals there can be seen a trend toward the specialization of functions unilaterally and a consequent greater dependence upon the tracts connecting these structures for coordination of these different functions.

R. D. Tschirgi[4] has hypothesized that the ideal primitive organism would be perfectly symmetrical (i.e. spheres, and their nervous systems having no axis of asymmetry would be totally unable to localize stimuli spatially). Accordingly, with the addition of axes of asymmetry, the nervous system would be able to reduce the spatial ambiguity about each new axis. Symmetry, then, implies loss of spatial information. Since the dominant symmetry in most higher animals is bilateral symmetry, there should therefore be the most ambiguity in localizing space about the *left right* dimension. This complies with common experience (i.e. we have not the slightest difficulty signaling head *vs.* toe or chest *vs.* back, but the parade ground in early drill practice testifies to the *left face vs. right face* ambiguities).

Is this then one of the prices that is paid for possessing two brains—the relative lack of ability to distinguish left and right?

A corollary to this question arises: would the artificial elimination of the last axis of symmetry therefore improve *left right* discrimination over the ability of the normal symmetrical animal?

In order to approach this question experimentally it was decided that the avian nervous system presented a favorable example for study. Not only do birds possess two rather independent bilateral systems, with very few connections between brain halves, but they are also intelligent, active animals which lends them discrimination training, using instrumental conditioning *(Skinner box)* techniques in which perceptual questions can be indirectly asked. In addition, birds are very resilient to surgical insults, far beyond that of other common laboratory animals. Homing pigeons were used exclusively.

The visual system was chosen for study because of the ease with which discrete, controlled stimuli could be administered and the relatively large body of anatomical knowledge which exists about this system. Within the visual system the asymmetrizing or unilateral damage was inflicted at one of three levels: the peripheral (the retina), the midbrain (the optic tectum), or the forebrain. Three birds had the retina of one eye destroyed; seven had one entire forebrain half removed, a procedure which did not affect them in any outward way at any time after surgery. In addition fifteen birds had a substantial portion of the optic midbrain removed on one side, while eight were left untouched as normal controls for comparison. In all ablated animals the only detectable deficit was unilateral blindness. (Fig. 1 indicates the sites of damage in comparison with a normal pigeon brain).

All experimental groups were then fasted until they had lost 20% of their free feeding weight (an empirically determined figure to insure their ready performance in the training task). They were then started in a

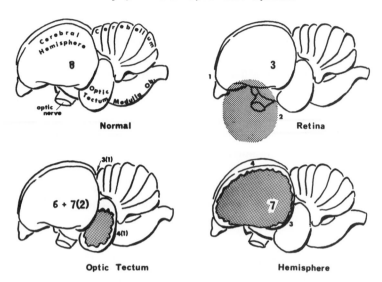

Figure 1. Sites of damage compared to normal brain.

standard pigeon *Skinner box* (Fig. 2) and led to peck on either of two lighted keys (two small dark openings on upper portion of internal panel) for food reinforcement (delivered at the square opening just below the two keys).

Figure 2. Standard *Skinner Box*

The animals were to be asked to differentiate left from right, an entirely different task from merely indicating left and right by reacting directly toward given stimuli. The pigeons were given a language of two abstract symbols, the color green and the color red to signal in response to two spatial stimuli, a light on the left or a light on the right. A simple switching apparatus (Fig. 3) was used to program automatically the sequence

Figure 3. Switching apparatus for automatic programming of the sequence of experimental events.

of events outlined in Fig. 4, in which a spatially oriented cue light was first presented, followed by two colored keys with a random spatial relation to the preceding cue light. The pigeon was required to peck on one of

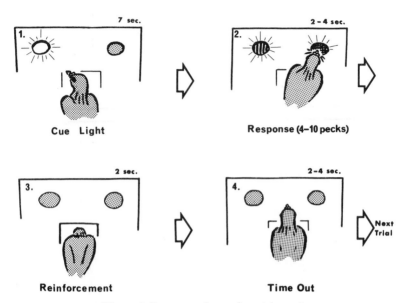

Figure 4. Sequence of experimental events.

the two colored keys and, if the bird pecked on the color that was appropriate for the spatial cue, a food reinforcement was delivered. If the bird pecked on the inappropriate color, the lights simply turned out until the next cue light presentation. Eighty-five such presentations and responses were permitted each day. Progress was noted by observing the percentage of correct responses per day over 50 percent which would mark random performance.

The results are shown graphically in Fig. 5. It can be clearly seen that the retinal-damaged animals performed at essentially the same level as the normal controls, while the birds with one hemisphere removed performed inferiorly. The startling thing, however, is the performance of the pigeons with one tectum damaged, which is considerably better than normal performance at all time beyond the second or third day (session). The differences between the forebrain damaged and normal birds and between the tectal damaged and normal birds tests statistically beyond the 1% level of significance.

Are these tectal damaged birds more *intelligent* than their intact brethren? Other studies in our laboratory indicate that the midbrain damaged animals do not perform better than normal animals in a simple brightness discrimination task nor even in the same task as this experiment, with the exception that the keys are vertically placed, one on top of the other.

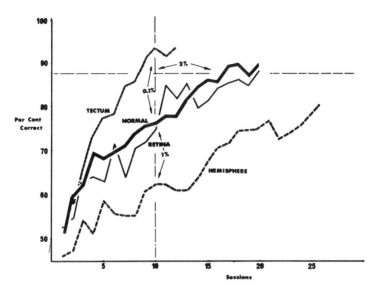

Figure 5. Experimental results.

Evidentally the improved performance is indeed related to the task demanded, to discrimination in the lateral or *left right* dimension. Perhaps
it is that the two symmetrically placed midbrain optic tecta exert a com-
petitive or mutually inhibitory influence on still higher centers giving rise
to ambiguity in evaluating input from these two sources. Perhaps also
this condition is chronic and must await the evolutionary appearance of
a totally asymmetric nervous system, yet with at least all of the advantages
inherit in the typical vertebrate bilateral pattern.

REFERENCES

1. R. W. Sperry, "Some Aspects of Interhemispheric Integration," in
   Interhemispheric Relations and Cerebral Dominance, Baltimore, Johns
   Hopkins Press, 1962.
2. J. Z. Young, "Why Do We Have Two Brains?," *ibid.*
3. H. Teuber, "Effects of Brain Wounds Implicating Right or Left Hemi-
   spheres," *Ibid.*
4. R. D. Tschirgi, "Spatial perception and central nervous system symmetry," *Arq. Neuropsiquiat., 16:* 363-66, 1958.

7

THE ELECTRICAL CONDUCTANCE OF SEMIPERMEABLE MEMBRANES*

L. J. BRUNER

Department of Physics,
University of California at Riverside

ABSTRACT

In a kinetic analysis of stationary ion flow within a homogeneous medium, one may take the flow of a given ion species to be proportional to the gradient of its concentration and to the electric field. The flow equations so obtained may be combined with Poisson's equation in such a way as to eliminate explicit dependence upon ion concentrations. The result of this process is a non-linear differential equation describing the spatial variation of the electric field (or displacement) which contains the ion currents as parameters. The order of the differential equation may be shown to depend upon the number of ion valence states present. It may also be demonstrated that, in equilibrium when the current flows are zero, the equation is equivalent to the corresponding Poisson-Boltzmann equation.

In applying this result to the problem of membrane conductance, we must consider three homogeneous media. These are the membrane, regarded as a plane laminar sheet of specified thickness, and the ionic solutions which bathe it on either side. Thus, the solution of the conductance

---

* A detailed account of this work is contained in a paper submitted to the *Biophysical Journal*.

problem reduces to the simultaneous solution of three non-linear differential equations (one for each of the three media) subject to appropriate
boundary conditions at the membrane-solution interfaces and within the
solution phases at large distance from the membrane. When these simultaneous solutions are obtained for a given stationary state of the system
they serve to fix the current parameters which enter into the equations,
and to fix the corresponding transmembrane potential as well. These solutions can only be obtained by numerical methods, necessitating the use
of digital computing equipment.

Our model for the membrane system is, of necessity, a particularly simple one. We assume that:

1. The membrane is a plane sheet of specified thickness, but
    of infinite extent in all directions parallel to its surfaces. Thus
    we deal with a problem of one-dimensional flow.
2. The membrane is impermeable to the solvent in the surround-
    ing solutions.
3. The membrane contains no bound charge.
4. Ions are classified, without consideration of the mechanisms
    involved, as permeable or impermeable. Permeable ions have
    finite mobilities different from zero within the membrane.
    Impermeable ion have zero mobility within the membrane
    and are excluded therefrom.
5. The surrounding solutions offer no impedance to the ion
    motion.
6. The solution phases are of infinite extent. Thus the ion con-
    centration at large distance from the membrane are unaffected
    by a stationery current flow, always maintaining their equili-
    brium values.

Our treatment of boundary conditions is based upon the following assertions:

1. Electric fields and ion concentration gradients must vanish
    in the solution phases at large distance from the membranes.
2. The permeable ion concentration is a continuous function of
    position everywhere.
3. The impermeable ion concentration drops discontinuously
    from a finite value to zero at the solution-membrane inter-
    faces.

These assertions establish the continuity of the electric displacement everywhere and permit the evaluation of the discontinuities in the displacement gradients at the solution-membrane interfaces.

This formulation of the problem of membrane conductance, although it suffers from the disadvantage that an analytic expression for the conductance cannot be obtained, is nonetheless relatively free of arbitrary assumptions regarding charge and field distributions in the vicinity of the membrane. Thus it is anticipated that comparison of theoretical predictions with experimental results on simple membranes should provide an indication of the inherent limitations of a kinetic description.

8

EXPERIMENTS ON A NEURONAL CONTROL NETWORK

GEORGE P. MOORE

University of California at Los Angeles

ABSTRACT

The activity of neuronal circuits involved in the control of respiration illustrates certain general or abstract properties of neural systems which strongly parallel features of perceptrons and self-organizing systems.

The neuro-respiratory system, in fact, shows all the essential features of the entire nervous system. It is subject to both neuronal and hemoral influence; it is dependent on both immediate and long term sensory feedback; its neural elements are capable of generating a broad spectrum of output which is patterned and repetitive, and determined not only by the immediate input but by the past history and predictable future of the organism. The system as a whole is clearly adaptive, and it can show plastic properties suggestive of short and long term memory. The internal organization of the system itself shares certain general features with self-organizing systems.*

---

* Moore presented examples of these shared features, together with results of recent experimental work which has elucidated some of the mechanisms underlying the activity of the neuro-respiratory system. [ED.]

9

THE ECONOMICS OF NEURAL SYSTEMS MODELING

H. J. HAMILTON

Librascope Division, General Precision Inc.
Glendale, California

ABSTRACT

From an economic point of view, scientific research is not fundamentally distinct from any other human enterprise. Its products, i.e., knowledge or theories, are produced at a cost; they are traded and evaluated in a market place; and, in their turn, are consumed in the construction of new or modified theories. The scientist, not unlike the entrepreneur, is at least vaguely aware that intellectual productivity, i.e., the increment of theoretical advance per man hour, must exceed some minimum level consistent with the goals of research in order to insure success and continued support from public and private sources. It is this realization perhaps more than anything else which prompts the scientist to search for a greater and greater economy of thought in theoretical expression as was observed in the last century by Ernst Mach. And it is this same concern which has motivated Warren Weaver[1] in recent times to question the power of existing theoretical tools when applied to "problems of organized complexity."

The difficulties which Weaver has enunciated are exemplified in the modeling of neural systems. On the basis of recent work by E. R. Lewis[2], it is now possible to account for virtually all of the observed diverse forms of electrical behavior of neurons in terms of a unified model of nerve membrane involving approximately seventeen parameters. This does not mean that the behavior of any neuron can be described in terms of seventeen parameters but only that the activity of any particular region or locus of neuronal membrane may be so described. In some cases, several loci may interact in such a manner as to require more elaborate specification in order to account for the total behavior of certain cells. The neuron thus appears as an extremely complex mechanism though it must be admitted that the significance of these various modes of behavior in processing information is not yet clear. Nevertheless, the problems posed for the development of a general theory relating structure and function in nervous systems are immense.

To appreciate the nature of these difficulties one need not consider large ganglia. To model a two-element system with reciprocal inhibitory connections would require approximately forty parameters (including the specification of input stimulus and axonal delays). Allowing each parameter to assume only one of three values, there would be a total of 3^{40} or approximately 10^{19} regions of the parameter space to explore. Not all of these regions will, of course, be interesting (even from a purely theoretical point of view) and quite probably only a rather limited domain will be of interest to the physiologist with specific questions in mind. But the point is this: the free ranging theorist cannot know, a priori, which regions of the parameter space for such a complex system merit intensive study. His only recourse as it now appears is to construct and probe physical or symbolic models to see what they will do. And it is clear that he could spend a lifetime in the systematic exploration of such models and never fully comprehend their behavior. A general or complete theory of such mechanisms in parametric detail appears to be beyond comprehension.

The physiologist or the theorist with certain specific and well formulated questions, on the other hand, can profit from model building and I have no doubt that significant progress will be made along these lines in the years to come. But the approach is not wholly satisfying; a general theory in some sense and at some level is needed to guide the construction and testing of models. The accumulation of partially explored models and half answered questions can hardly facilitate economy of thought or intellectual productivity to the degree called for if we are ever to attain a comprehensive understanding of animal nervous systems.

What will be the form of such a theory is a matter for speculation but it would appear that it must be confined to a description of very broad structural and behavioral properties while yet providing relatively explicit instructions for the construction of detailed models.

REFERENCES

1. Warren Weaver, "Science and Complexity," *American Scientist,* October, 1948.
2. E. R. Lewis, "The Ionic Hypothesis as a Unifying Basis of Neuronal Behavior," paper to be submitted to *J. Theor. Biology.*

10

A LEARNING NETWORK MODEL

ROGER A. STAFFORD

Philco Corporation
Newport Beach, California

INTRODUCTION

Although modern electronic digital computers are able to perform very rapid calculations on large amounts of data, far exceeding humans in both speed and accuracy, they are still used primarily for procedures that can be specified by relatively simple, iterative means. Problems such as the recognition of visual patterns, theorem proving, devising game strategy, and natural language translation remain very difficult to program for these computers.

There is an interesting similarity between the structure of computers and that of the human brain. The electronic circuitry of computers, involving flip-flop elements interconnected so as to have certain logical relationships, is analogous to the neural networks in brain matter. There remain many basic differences, however, and two of these will be noted here. First, the human brain is far more complex in terms of the number of elements and their interconnections. Second, there are indications that brains are capable of altering their interconnection "logic" so as to more properly respond to an encountered environment. Present day computers possess no such ability. The subject of this paper is an attempt to overcome this second deficiency. The term "learning network" refers to computer-like networks which in some way are to possess this ability to alter the logic of their interconnections in response to inputs from an *environment*. It is possible that such networks may be able to arrive by adaptation at interconnection logic of a greater complexity than it is practical for a person to specifically design into a fixed network.

In this paper, a learning network will mean a network of computing elements which can receive a set of inputs and produce a set of outputs in response to them. If these outputs are inappropriate, then the network is to receive error signals setting into motion an internal change which is to alter the logical nature of the network and to produce correct outputs for the given inputs. If these internal changes are well made, the network should have the ability, after a sufficient number of mistakes, to respond with correct outputs to each of the input sets.

SINGLE THRESHOLD ELEMENTS

It is assumed that the elements of which the network is composed are linear threshold elements which receive a set of two-state variables, $x_1, x_2, \ldots x_n$, and produce a single two-state variable, y. Each element possesses a set of variable quantities, $c_0, c_1, \ldots c_n$, which can assume any real values. These determine y by the rule: $y = +1$ *if* $c_0 + c_1x_1 + \ldots + c_nx_n$ is positive, and otherwise $y = -1$. It is assumed that the x_i's are each $+1$ or -1 in value. The c-values, or weights as they will be referred to, constitute the adjustable part of a learning network composed of these elements.

A single threshold element possesses some of the properties required for an entire learning network if it uses the following error-correcting rule:

> whenever the element produces an incorrect output for a set of inputs, its weights are adjusted according to the rule $\Delta c_0 = y^*$, $\Delta c_i = y^*x_i$, $i = 1, 2, \ldots, n$, where y^* is the desired output.

Since the linear combination above changes by the increment $\Delta(c_0 + c_1x_1 + \ldots + c_nx_n) = (n+1)y^*$, it is clear that y *will be equal to* y^* after enough of these increments. It has been proven that if there exist sets of weights which will produce the correct y for each of the required input sets, then the weight correction procedure given here has the property that after these inputs have been repeated a sufficient number of times, one of these successful sets of weights will be arrived at, regardless of the initial values used.

However, the logical capability of such a single element is very limited. That is, for most specified functions, $y = f(x_1, x_2, \ldots, x_n)$, no set of weights exists which will generate the function with a single element. For example, with $n = 6$, only one in each 10^{12} functions can be so realized in a 7-weight single threshold element.

MULTIPLE-ELEMENT NETWORKS

In order to obtain a large variety of possible output responses to inputs it is necessary to combine a number of threshold elements in a network, the outputs of some serving as inputs to others along with the inputs to the network. The study in this paper will be restricted to networks with only a single final output variable on which the error signal is based.

In such a network, once it has been determined that a given element is to have its output altered, the same rule as given above will be used to correct its weights. The central problem will be that of determining what set of elements to correct, since the error signal will indicate only that the network as a whole is incorrect. In the following paragraphs a number of qualitative features will be described which, on the basis of empirical evidence, are likely to be necessary in any successful method.

As many computer simulations have shown, it is essential to minimize the effect on previously learned input-output combinations when correcting an error. Hence, it is important to choose a minimum number of elements for weight change. Any alterations of more than this number of elements may increase the damage being done to previous learning.

Another principle which appears to lessen this damage is to select elements for weight change whose sums are relatively close to zero so that not many weight increments are required to reverse their outputs. These are the elements which will undergo the smallest amount of logical change for other input combinations.

In a reasonably complicated network it is necessary to ascertain whether a given contemplated change is likely to be useful or not. This can be accomplished by making tentative changes in the network itself in order to see whether or not the output is corrected. That is, the network itself is used for evaluating the efficacy of changes before they are made permanent. As will be seen in one of the specific models described later, this testing is mandatory in order to avoid making changes which are actually harmful.

It is apparently necessary to provide networks with a margin of complexity somewhat in excess of the minimum required to achieve the functions which are to be learned. Without this excess there are too few weight combinations which can realize the desired function, and it becomes difficult for a learning procedure to find such a combination. Even in the case of a single element, this is true with respect to putting constraints on the possible weight levels each weight can assume. With too tight a constraint on weight levels, a solution may not ever be attained by the learning process for a single element, even if a solution exists and satisfies this constraint.

In making the decision as to which elements to alter in an error-correcting process, a maximum amount of use should be made of the already existing computing capacity in the network. The use of a centralized *element selector* is to be avoided, since this would require an excessive amount of interconnections with the network. Instead, a method should be used which allows the decision-making to be performed as autonomously as possible by individual elements.

TWO MODELS

In the previous section some qualitative requirements were put forth. In this section two specific models are given which satisfy these. The first model requires that all weights attached to inputs of an element which come from other elements (i.e., the interconnecting weights) be kept positive. Then, changing any element's output will tend to change the final output in the same direction. This makes it easy to avoid harmful changes. This is done by changing the outputs of elements only in that direction desired for the final output.

Each element is provided with a common value, b, which is added to that element's sum. Ordinarily $b=0$, and therefore has no effect. However, if the network's output is in error, b commences to change continuously in the direction of the desired output. This will cause elements, in a sequence depending on the magnitude of their sums, to change so as to agree with the desired final output. Eventually the final output will be corrected.

At this point b commences to return toward zero. Whenever the final output becomes incorrect, there will be an element in the network whose sum has just passed through zero and whose change caused the chain effect which changed the final output. This element is then subjected to a correcting weight change which renders the final output correct. The value b then continues toward zero, stopping each time the output becomes incorrect long enough to correct the offending element whose sum passed through zero. When b finally reaches zero with the correct final output, the network is ready for the next input.

It should be noted that this model satisfies each of the previously mentioned requirements reasonably well. It tends to minimize tne number of elements subjected to weight change, because none are changed without demonstrating that each could cause an error. Those elements with small sums tend to be selected because b goes only as far from zero as is necessary to correct the output. Each element is tested for its effect on the final output if its sum goes through zero, and it is corrected only if it has such an effect. Finally this procedure allows the decision to be nearly autonomous, requiring only that information about b, the desired final output, and the error signal be furnished to each element. The only centralized activity required is that of changing b properly.

A second model is described here which differs in some respects from the first one. The restriction as to positive values for the interconnecting weights is removed. Dropping this restriction requires the use of a more complicated perturbation of the network than the previous single quantity, b. This is because a large number of combinations of directions must be tried in order to be sure of finding one which efficiently corrects the output. That is, many combinations of directions contain some harmful changes and might be very inefficient ones to use.

The second model accomplishes this by assuming that a common quantity b is given to each element as before (except that now it is always non-negative), but that each element generates its own randomly varying sign which is multiplied by b before being added to the element's sum. As these elements' signs vary during a corrective process, and as b increases from zero, the effect on the network involves an increasing number of elements in a wide variety of combinations. This should be sufficient to eventually correct the output.

Once the output is correct, these signs become frozen while b decreases toward zero. Then the corrective process commences exactly as in the first model except that the sign (now fixed) of each element rather than the desired final output is used to determine the direction of change of the element's weights. When b has reached zero with a correct final output, the signs are unfrozen and the network is ready for another input.

It will be noted that this method still has the advantages possessed by the first model. In the particular combination of temporarily altered elements which first produces the correct output, not all of these elements must be subjected to weight change. If some are not found to be directly responsible for a failure, their weights remain unchanged.

COMPUTER SIMULATION

At the time of this paper, a computer program for the IBM 7090 simulating the first of the two models has been prepared and about 2,000 learning trials have been performed using four-input and six-input logic functions and a variety of network configurations. The program is being revised to allow testing of the second model.

The results of the tests on the first model will not be described in detail here because they are incomplete. However, two important points are already evident. The first is that learning network models have advanced sufficiently to be able to learn quite complicated functions with relatively few repeated errors. In most of the experiments, six-input functions were to be learned whose truth table was randomly chosen, and the networks used for these usually consisted of 12 elements. The number of errors per learning trial in most of these averaged about 150, which is worse than a perfect learning device by a factor of 4 or 5 to 1 (there being 64 input combinations to be learned, half of which should be right the first time on the average). When 20 elements were used, this average dropped to about 100, showing the effect on learning rates of an increase in the total number of variable weights.

The second point is that the restriction to positive values for interconnecting weights seems to impair their usefulness more than had been expected. Experiments were performed which compared the performance of networks in which a certain set of its interconnecting weights were used in some trials and removed in others. The results failed to show any striking impairment in performance with their removal. However, a similar removal of some of the other kind of weights (those which were attached to the basic inputs to the network and which were allowed to become negative) produced a great deterioration of performance.

The results of these and other experiments strongly point to the need for experimentation with the second model in order to see if the interconnecting weights become significantly more effective when they are allowed negative values.

CONCLUSIONS

In most investigations of learning networks, there are strong restrictions placed on their structure. In particular, the elements with variable weights usually all occur on the same layer (i.e., no one of them receives the output of another of them.) For example, the simple perceptron investigated by F. Rosenblatt [1] involves a first layer of elements with fixed weights and a single adjustable element in the second layer receiving their outputs. B. Widrow's Madeline [2] uses a first layer of many adjustable elements whose outputs go into a single fixed element in the second layer. The models described in this paper are part of an attempt to develop learning networks of a more general structure, using many adjustable layers.

The empirical evidence obtained with the first model indicates that such multi-layer networks can indeed succeed in learning non-trivial functions. However, they do not, so far, exceed the performance of the more restrictive networks described above when the numbers of variable weights are comparable.

REFERENCES

1. F. Rosenblatt, *Principles of Neurodynamics; Perceptrons and the Theory of Brain Mechanism,* Spartan Books, Washington, D.C., 1962.

2. W. C. Ridgway, "An Adaptive Logic System with Generalizing Properties," Stanford Electronic Laboratories, Tech. Report No. 1556-1, April 1962.

11

A FORMAL THEORY OF PROBLEM-SOLVING*

E. Mark Gold

Sloan Mathematics Center
Stanford University
California

1. INTRODUCTION

Let the term *thinking machine* refer to any device which can replace a human at tasks which are intuitively considered to require intelligence. Such a device must be able to learn simple rules without fail, such as, *i* before *e* except after *c* and few other exceptions, and it must be capable of occasionally solving a difficult problem which would be considered *creative* if performed by a human (an example from electronics is the invention of the travelling wave tube in order to achieve wideband amplification).

More specifically, the object of this research is the construction of a mathematical model of thinking, both of the environments in which it takes place and of the methods by which it can be accomplished. The goal is a theory with at least sufficient power to allow, as one application, the design of a machine with the ability to learn a natural language and make use of information presented in this language to formulate answers which appear intelligent to a questioner. Its training is to be of the same type as that received by a human, rather than the detailed programming in an *a priori* computer language required by present-day computers.

---

* This work was performed by the author while at LSI Research Labs and at The RAND Corporation, both in Santa Monica, Calif.

This research proceeds as follows: a class of environments is defined, each containing a goal to be achieved by the *thinker*. A minimum level of goal achievement is specified, and then the thinker is asked if there is a single *thinking* algorithm which will adapt to any of the environments to the required degree. If so, the next question is, how do the limitations of practical computation, such as memory capacity, affect these conclusions? Since learning is an important part of thinking, analagous methods are being employed to investigate information learning situations (as opposed to behaviour-learning which characterizes goal-seeking). The results of this work have been reported in detail.[1, 2, 3] The two most interesting phases of this research will be reviewed here.

The second section is concerned with a general model of goal-seeking. This type of model is considered to be general enough to include every type of behaviour which is generally called thinking; however, it turns out that there is no such thing as a universal thinker, one which will adapt to some degree to any environment in which it finds itself. On the basis of the simple results of this investigation, and subsequent failure to find any alternative approach of comparable generality which would allow a general solution, it would appear that a unified theory of artificial intelligence is impossible. That is, it will never be possible to say that *such and such* is the goal of thinking, and here is a method for accomplishing it. Rather, special types of problems must be considered individually in order to find *thinkers* specific to these classes of problems.

An example of this approach is presented in the third section, which discusses the identification of a set of positive integers on the basis of successive pieces of information which tell whether or not specific positive integers belong to the set. This investigation was motivated by the problem of learning a language. As a specific example of its application, suppose one wants to learn which strings of symbols from an *a priori* specified alphabet are considered grammatically correct in a certain language. If a positive integer is assigned to every possible string in a *one to one* manner, the problem of learning a language reduces to that of identifying a set of positive integers. A number of models of set identification are considered. These involve various methods of presentation of the information about the set, meant to model the circumstances under which a human learns a natural language. The main result of this research is that it is not possible to learn languages of nontrivial classes solely from a text. An informant is necessary, the difference being that a text can only give examples of grammatically correct sentences, it cannot explicitly indicate that a sentence is not grammatically correct.

2.　A GENERAL MODEL OF GOAL-SEEKING

This research is motivated by the following practical problem. A machine is to be devised whose inputs and outputs will consist solely of English words and punctuation. First, the machine is to learn English from examples given to it, as does a human. *Learning English* is taken to mean that it is to learn those rules of *well formedness,* logic, meaning, pragmatics, etc., which can be formalized with no reference to other than linguistic concepts. Second, the machine is to undergo a training program in English which will teach it, both explicitly and implicity, the rules which determine what sort of statements by the machine are likely to be of interest to the operator. The third stage in the life of a thinking machine is that in which it attempts to say something impressive (to the operator). The operator has means for signalling approval or disapproval to the machine. Of course the three stages will not be clear-cut, nor is the above description meant to be precise. The purpose of the description is to provide motivation for the choice of models of thinking behavior to be investigated.

Since the purpose of the machine is to please the operator, the sole criterion of its intelligence is the amount of reward it receives. The general situation is illustrated in Fig. 1. T represents the thinker and $U + G$ (universe and goal) represents the thinker's environment. T produces an output, o, on the basis of the inputs from its environment: the information input, i, and the reward or punishment signal, v (value). Time is taken to be quantized, $n = 1, 2, \ldots$, and at each time a single symbol passes along each communication channel, drawn from the alphabet corresponding to the channel:

$$o_n \; \epsilon \; O \qquad i_n \; \epsilon \; I \qquad v_n \; \epsilon \; V$$

Due to the linguistic motivation of this work, each alphabet is assumed to be finite. V is ordered, but O and I give no *priori* structure. O and I gain meaning for the thinker as it learns the relationships between o, i, and v determined by $U+G$. The objective is to design the thinker so that it will receive high values of v as often as possible.

$U+G$ is no more than a function which determines the present value of i and v, i_n and v_n, in terms of the past history of o. Such a function is called a black box. More precisely, a black box will signify the following triple: a finite input set X, containing at least two elements; a finite output set Y, containing at least two elements; and an input-output function, **b**, namely, a string function which determines the output, $y_n \epsilon Y$, at each time n in terms of the input history $x_1, \ldots, x_{n-1} \epsilon X$. T is also a black box; its input and output sets are the opposite of those of $U+G$.

$U+G$ will henceforth be referred to as the universe. The type of problem which has been investigated is as follows [3]: A class of universes is

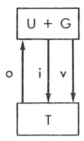

Figure 1. The general goal-seeking situation.

specified. A minimum level of goal achievement, possibly depending on the universe, is defined and an allowable class of thinkers is given. It is then asked whether or not there is a thinker of the allowed type which will adapt to any universe of the specified class to the required degree, that is the v_n it receives will be sufficiently high.

The fundamental idea behind this type of model, namely the identification of intelligence with goal-seeking ("If you're so smart, why aren't you rich?"), occurs often, in diverse forms, in the artificial intelligence literature. However, in this field the models are rarely made explicit. One feature of this model, however, is unusual: The concept of adaption requires an uncertainty concerning the universe. This is introduced by considering a class of possible universes. Each is deterministic, and the thinker will be confronted with only one of them. The usual method of introducing uncertainty is to consider a probabilistic universe (see, for example, Tsetlin [4]). Considering the amount of effort which has been devoted to the study of probabilistic situations, particularly in learning theory, it is interesting to note that deterministic situations are far from trivial.

Three types of black boxes will be considered: *FA* (finite state automata), primitive recursive, and recursive. An *FA black box* is one which can be realized by a real computer, that is a computer with a finite, initially fixed memory. Due to the fact that the computer can not be allowed to go into an unending cycle, that is, it cannot repeat a state, and the fact that it has finite memory, it is easy to show that here is a maximum number of computations which will be necessary for the computer to compute the black box output after it has received an input. Note that an *FA black box* must have finite input and output alphabets. *A recursive black box* is one such that there is an algorithm which will compute what its output will be after any specified input string. Thus, in order to realize a recursive black box, one must use a computer with infinite memory, and, even though the number of computations required to compute an output must be finite, there is not necessarily a maximum number of computations. The *primitive recursive black boxes* are a sub-class of the recursive black boxes and include all the *FA black boxes*. The following gives a very crude idea of their definition: in order to realize a primitive recursive black box one requires, as in the general case of recursive black boxes, a computer with infinite memory and the ability to make an unbounded number of computations to compute each output. However, the number of computations for any specified input string can be predicted in advance.

It was intended to show that thinkers exist which can adapt in some reasonable sense to any of a general class of universes. For instance, it seemed reasonable to expect to be able to demonstrate an *FA* thinker realizable by a computer with one million bits of memory which could eventually learn enough of the rules of any recursive universe, or at least any *FA* universe, to obtain v_n at least as high as the best *FA* thinker (for that universe) with, say, 1000 bits of memory. However, it turned out that no matter how weakly *adaptation* is defined, results of this type are impossible. That is to say, given any thinker, no matter how well designed, there is a universe of roughly the same complicatedness as the thinker for which the thinker will always do the worst possible thing.

More precisely, the following was shown: if the thinker is *FA*, then there is a universe whose V alphabet is [0,1] with the usual ordering, such that this particular thinker will receive $v_n=0$ for all n, but if it were to produce any different value of 0_n at any time n it would receive $v_n=1$, for all subsequent n, no matter what it were to do henceforth. Furthermore, this universe can be realized by a computer with at most one more bit of memory than the thinker. Similarly, if the thinker were primitive recursive or recursive, then such a primitive recursive or recursive universe is possible. Once stated precisely, these theorems are trivial to prove.

It seems reasonable to expect some degree of adaption to be possible in cases in which the universe is restricted to being significantly simpler than the thinker. As an example in this direction, the following theorem has been proven: if the thinker is allowed to be primitive recursive and the class of *FA* universes is specified, then there is a thinker which will adapt to any of the universes in a very strong sense.

3. LANGUAGE IDENTIFICATION IN THE LIMIT

In order to define what is meant by *identifying a language,* it is first necessary to state what aspects of a language are to be identified. The only feature of a language to be considered here is the syntactic property of being grammatically correct. Therefore, given a finite alphabet, *specifying a language* means specifying which strings of symbols are grammatically accepted by this language. A language will here mean no more than a distinguished subset of the set of all possible strings on this alphabet. This naive concept of a language will be considered in the following abstract form. A positive integer is to be assigned to each string on the alphabet in a *one to one* manner; a natural way of doing so will be specified later. The set of strings on the alphabet is thereby identified with the set of positive integers; so that a *language* comes to mean a subset of the set of all positive integers.

The following is an example of the sort of situation visualized under the heading of identifying a language. The *identifier* is presented, starting from an initial time, with an unending sequence of information about the language from an *informant,* whose job is to tell the identifier whether or not successive numbers are elements of the language (some set of positive integers). Three methods for choosing the sequence of positive integers about which the informant is to give information are specified and investigated below. The identifier, on the basis of the successive information given to him by the informant, produces a sequence of guesses as to the identity of the language. For instance, his goal may be to find a decision procedure for the language, i.e., an algorithm which will allow one to determine whether or not any given positive integer is a number of the language. This method of specifying a language will be called a *tester* for the language. The identifier will be said to have *identified the language in the limit* if, after some finite time (not pre-determined), his guesses are not only invariably correct, but also identical (it is possible that there is more than one tester for a language, i.e., more than one algorithm for determining whether or not numbers belong to the language).

The purpose of introducing the concept of identification in the limit is that it is much more powerful than the usual concept of a finite identification experiment, which requires that the identifier stop the experiment after some finite time (at his discretion) and give the identity of the unknown object. The user of a limiting identification procedure will not necessarily know when his guesses are correct, but he can be confident that after some finite time, if his guesses serve some purpose, he will be acting on correct information. Identification in the limit has occasionally appeared in the pattern recognition literature, for example, Aizerman et al [5], but to my knowledge has not previously been given a name.

A number of models of language identification will be presented. For each model, it is necessary to state (a) how information about the language is to be presented to the identifier, and (b) how the identifier is to state the identity of the language. As to the first, besides an *informant,* described in the above example, a *text* is also considered as a possible method of presenting information. By a text is meant an unending sequence of positive integers chosen from the language, such that every positive integer of the language occurs at least once in the text. Thus, the difference between an informant and a text is that an informant can specifically tell the identifier that a certain positive integer is not in the language, but a text cannot. It is necessary to specify further how the examples may be chosen in order to form a text. Three variations are considered which, together with the three types of informants, yield a total of six methods of information presentation to be investigated.

As to the second problem, that is, how the identity of the language may be specified, two methods are considered. Instead of the *tester,* described in the above example, the identifier may be required to guess a *generator* for the language; that is, an algorithm which allows one to generate an endless sequence of positive integers, such that each one is a member of the language, and all positive integers of the language are eventually generated. In total, 12 models of language identification are investigated (six methods of information presentation and two of language specification).

Suppose now that a certain class of languages is specified, together with one of the 12 models of identification. Is there an algorithm which the identifier may use to generate his guesses such that, if he is being presented with information about one of the languages in the prescribed class, it can be guaranteed that after some finite time his guesses will all be the same and correct? If such an algorithm is possible, then it will be said that this class of languages is *identifiable in the limit* with respect to this particular model of language identification.

Note that the question does not ask whether or not a specific language is *identifiable in the limit.* Rather, this term is applied only to classes of languages. Saying that a class of languages is not limiting identifiable implies nothing about specific languages of the class. Given some identifier algorithm, it is possible that any specific language of the class will be quickly identified by a lucky guess. As an example, suppose a model of language identification is considered in which information is presented by a text. Then the class of languages is *not* limiting identifiable if, given any guessing algorithm for identifying languages, there is a language of the class, and an infinitely long text of the allowed type which includes every element of the language, such that the guessing algorithm fails to identify the language in the following sense: if, given some finite segment of the text, the algorithm correctly guesses the identity of the language, then there is a longer finite segment of the text, containing the original one, which the rule will interpret to produce the wrong guess.

From a practical standpoint, linguists have proven the informant to be a reliable source from which to learn a language. Indeed, in the six models of language identification from an informant discussed here, context free languages, which are of great interest to linguists as models of natural languages, have been found to be limiting identifiable. However, most linguists attempting to develop automatic methods of language analysis assume that information will be given by a text. The question then arises, "Can languages be identified from text?" Theorems have now been proven which show that, except in one model which appears completely unrealistic (generator identification from primitive recursive text), only the most trivial classes of languages are limiting identifiable from text.

The remainder of this section will be devoted to a more detailed description of the models of language identification and the results obtained. Let L signify a language, that is, a set of positive integers. The two methods by which the identifier may be required to specify a language are as follows: A *tester* for L denotes a number, g, which is the Gödel number of a Turing machine that is a decision procedure for the language; that is to say, the function defined by the gth Turing machine, Z_g, is the characteristic function, X_L, of L. A *generator* for L denotes a number, g, such that Z_g is total, i.e., Z_g (x) is defined for every x, and $L = Rng$ (Z_g).* Thus testers can only be used to specify recursive sets and generators can only be used to specify recursively enumerable sets. In either case each guess, g_n, produced by the identifier will be a number.

The six methods by which information may be presented to the identifier are as follows. A *text* for L denotes an infinite sequence of numbers, $x_1, x_2, \ldots$, perhaps with repetitions, such that $L = Rng$ (x_n). The three types of text are *arbitrary, recursive,* and *primitive recursive*: An arbitrary text may be any sequence, x_n, which ranges over L. In the case of a recursive text it is required that an algorithm exist for computing the sequence x_n. As with black boxes, a primitive recursive text is a special case of a recursive text.

An *informant* for L is an infinite sequence of ordered pairs of numbers, $(z_1, t_1), (z_2, t_2), \ldots$, where $t_n = X_L(z_n)$. Thus, at time n the identifier is told either that z_n is an element of L if $t_n = 1$) or that it isn't (if $t_n = 0$). The three types of informant are methodical, arbitrary, and request. The *methodical informant* is required to have $z_n = n$, so that the identified may be told, for instance, that †

$$1 \notin L \quad 2 \notin L \quad 3 \notin L \quad 4 \notin L \quad \ldots \quad n \notin L \quad \ldots$$

In the case of an *arbitrary informant,* z_n may be any function of n such that z_n takes on every possible value at least once. In the case of the *request informant,* z_n is to be specified by the identifier.

The *identifier* consists of (a) a guessing algorithm for generating at each time, n, a guess, g_n, as to a tester or generator for L on the basis of the information it has received through that time, and (b) in the case of information presentation by means of a request informant, a *questioning* algorithm for generating z_n as a function of the information received through time n.

As an example of the 12 models, a class, C, of languages is called *limiting generator identifiable from recursive text* if there is an identifier with the following property: Let L be any language of C. Then, given any recursive text for L, there is some finite time after which the identifier will always produce the same guess and this will be a generator for L.

The limiting identifiability properties of the following classes of languages have been investigated: (a) recursively enumerable, (b) recursive, (c) primitive recursive, (d) *FA* (regular), and (e) finite. By a finite language is meant one which contains but a finite number of elements. An *FA* language is one such that it is possible to design a real computer which will determine whether or not any given positive integer is an element of the language. A recursive language is one such that there is an algorithm for determining whether or not any given integer is an element of the language. The primitive recursive languages are a sub-class of the recursive languages and include the *FA* languages. A recursively enumerable language is one such that there exists an algorithm which will generate all the elements of the language, that is, the algorithm defines a function whose range is the language. Note that the recursively enumerable languages include the recursive languages which include the primitive recursive languages which include the *FA* languages which include the finite languages. Since the void set cannot be specified by a generator nor presented by means of a text (both are required to be total functions), it is assumed to be omitted from all classes in those models of language identification that have either of these properties.

The results of this investigation are summarized in Table 1. Of course, if a certain class of languages is shown to be limiting identifiable in one of the 12 models, then the same holds for any smaller class; and, if it is not limiting identifiable, then the same holds for all larger classes.

The concept of recursively enumerable, recursive, or primitive recursive set are of *number theoretic* origin. However, that of *FA* or context-free is of linguistic origin and is normally applied only to a set of finite strings on some finite alphabet. Recall that for each alphabet, A, a *one to one* enumeration is assumed to assign a number to each finite string on A. Thus, a set of numbers, L, corresponds to many sets of strings, one for each choice of A. A linguistic property, such as FA or context-free, will be applied to L to signify that at least one of these string-sets has this property.

Note that which sets of numbers are, for example, FA depends on the choice of method of assigning numbers to the strings on A, where A ranges over all alphabets. It is assumed that the enumeration is obtained by ordering the strings first according to length, and then alphabetically. With this enumeration, the class of context-free languages is a proper subclass of the class of primitive recursive languages, and properly includes the class of FA languages.

TABLE 1. Limiting identifiability of languages

Type of Presentation	Method of Identification	The following classes are limiting identifiable	are not limiting identifiable
arbitrary informant ⎫		primitive	
methodical informant ⎬ equivalent*	generator	recursive	recursive
request informant ⎭			
arbitrary informant ⎫		primitive	
methodical informant ⎬ equivalent*	tester	recursive	recursive
request informant ⎭		recursively	
primitive recursive text	generator	enumerable	. . .
primitive recursive text	tester	finite	FA
recursive text	generator	finite	FA
recursive text	tester	finite	FA
arbitrary text	generator	finite	FA
arbitrary text	tester	finite	FA

Note: With any type of presentation of information, and given any class of sets, limiting tester identifiable $\Longrightarrow$ limiting generator identifiable.

* Models of language identification are called *equivalent* if exactly the same classes of sets are identifiable in both senses.

REFERENCES

1. E. Mark Gold, "Limiting Recursion," *Journal of Symbolic Logic,* to appear.

2. —— "Language Identification in the Limit," The RAND Corp., RM-4136-PR (July 1964).

3. —— "Miscellaneous Theorems, Hopefully Related to Artificial Intelligence," The RAND Corp., informal report available from the author (1964).

4. M. L. Tsetlin, "Games Between Automata," *Automation and Remote Control,* vol. 24 (1963), pp. 889-899.

5. M. A. Aizerman, E. M. Braverman, and L. I. Rozonoer, *Avtomatika i Telemekhanika,* vol. 25, No. 6 (1964), to be translated in *Automation and Remote Control.* See also "Probability Problem of Pattern Recognition Learning and Potential Functions Method," *Avtomatika i Telemekhanika,* vol. 25, No. 9 (1964), pp. 1307-1323.

12

TIME-VARYING THRESHOLD LOGIC

E. E. Nelson, J. A. Daly and R. D. Joseph

Astropower Electronics Laboratory
Missile & Space Systems Division
Douglas Aircraft Company, Inc.

INTRODUCTION

The use of linear logic threshold elements in current pattern recognition devices involves two major difficulties: such devices are capable of only two outputs, and the assignment of outputs to particular inputs is subject to the restraints of linear separability.[1]

There exists a device which avoids both of these shortcomings. A linear logic unit may be provided with a threshold varying in time over the entire range of possible input levels. A logic unit then turns on at a time directly determined by the input level. Depending on the nature of the weights assigned to the input connections, a unit with n binary inputs may have from $n + 1$ to 2^n distinct input levels. In the latter case, achieved by assigning weights proportional to powers of 2 to the connections, each possible binary input state has a unique weighted signal level. Thus the time of response of a logic unit may be made to specify exactly the input sub-pattern to the unit.

The proper utilization of this unit in a large system requires that the output weight associated with a logic unit vary synchronously with the threshold. To accomplish this, a system clock may be used to control the threshold and to specify the output weight.

Among the many possible approaches to time varying mechanizations,

101

the most promising appears to be one in which the threshold is varied in discrete steps. A resistor weighting network corresponding to each threshold is constructed, and the appropriate network sampled according to the control of the system clock. When a clock cycle has been completed, these sampled values may be added to determine the system response. The system required for this operation is shown in Fig. 1.

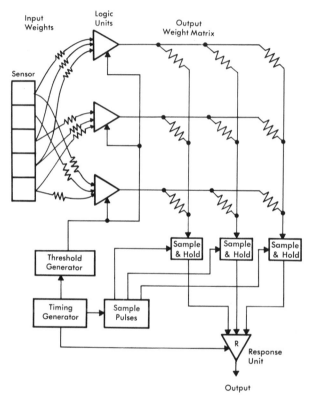

Figure 1. System block diagram.

At any specific value of the threshold, each logic unit partitions the signal space with a hyperplane. Points on one side of the hyperplane produce a one output from the logic unit; points on the other side produce a zero output. A change in the threshold results in a parallel displacement of the hyperplane. Each logic unit thus establishes a series of parallel hyperplanes in the signal space. The collection of all hyperplanes for all logic units partitions the signal space into cells. The design of the pattern classification device then becomes the specification of a partition such that the cells may be identified with unique classes of patterns.

The input weights, and hence the logic unit hyperplanes, are determined by the use of the discriminant analysis technique. Discriminant analysis is a well-established multivariate statistical technique.[2] For classification problems which meet the underlying assumptions, the technique provides an optimum decision rule for assigning observed sets of data points to one of several classes.

The assumptions basic to discriminant analysis are the following:

(a) The observation X is a vector chance variable. It is drawn from one of several multivariate normal distributors, depending only on its class membership.

(b) These distributions differ only in their unknown mean vectors. An unknown covariance matrix is common to all of the distributions.

(c) The decision criteria are to be based on sample vectors drawn randomly from each of the distributors.

For computational reasons, each logic unit is permitted only a small number of input connections (corresponding to nonzero coefficients of the hyperplanes). More units are generated than are used in the machine.

The selection of logic units to be incorporated in the machine is done sequentially in order to maximize the separation of pattern classes in the recognition space. In other words, units are added one at a time, each unit added to the machine being selected from a population of possible units by the criterion of maximum improvement of the interclass separations. This is accomplished by means of a loss function. In particular, the procedure selects for inclusion in the network that logic unit which provides the greatest decrease in minimum loss. In the generation and selection of logic units, the system gives more weight to misclassified and marginally classified patterns. Thus as many of the sample patterns are classified correctly as possible.

APPLICATION TO CHARACTER RECOGNITION

To demonstrate the effectiveness of this design procedure using time-varying threshold logic units, the technique was used in the simulated design of a character recognition device. The input patterns were a set of 240 handprinted (unregistered) alphabetic characters, divided into 12 classes with 20 characters in each class. The letters chosen were as follows: E, T, A, O, I, N, S, H, R, D, L and U. The sensory plane consisted of a

7×5 retina. A retinal element was considered active if any part of the pattern crossed the element.

INPUT WEIGHTS

The specification of the logic unit input weights was made by the application of the discriminant analysis technique. In this procedure, the principal eigenvector of the among pattern classes dispersion matrix (i.e., the covariance matrix for the class centroids) in a canonical space is taken to be the axis of maximum differentiation. A short summary of the process is given here.

The original signal space is reduced to a canonical space (in which the intraclass dispersion matrix is a unit matrix) by the linear transformation (column vectors are used).

$$Y = P'X$$

P is the matrix of eigenvectors of C_x, the pooled intraclass dispersion matrix. Each eigenvector is normalized to have length $1/\sqrt{\lambda_i}$, where λ_i is the corresponding eigenvalue.

Let A_x be the dispersion matrix of the class centroids in the original space. Then $P' A_x P$ is the dispersion matrix of the class means in the canonical space. Let V be the principal eigenvector (normalized to unit length) of $P' A_x P$, that is, the eigenvector of the largest eigenvalue of $P'A_x P$. V is the direction of the major axis of the ellipsoid of constant density defined by

$$y'(p'ap)^{-1}y = \text{constant}$$

The determination of the projection, z, of a vector, X, in the original space on the principal axis, V, is given by

$$z = V'P'X = X'PV$$

so that the coordinates of PV serve as the weights of the input connections to the logic unit.

The geometric significance of these quantities should be interpreted. The vector, PV, provides the coefficients of the discriminant function of the logic unit. It is the direction of the original space in which classes are most separable. Consequently, hyperplanes spaced along this axis would be expected to provide an optimal pattern separation.

THRESHOLD LEVELS

As previously mentioned, the principal eigenvector of the among-groups dispersion matrix is taken as the axis of maximum differentiation. The strategy used in the design of time varying threshold logic (TVTL) units is to pass a hyperplane through the space perpendicular to this axis, utilizing the threshold variation to slide the point of intersection along this axis.

After considering many possible procedures for placing the threshold levels, it was decided to use seven levels and the method illustrated in Fig. 2. This figure shows the average weighted inputs to the logic unit for each of the 12 classes. It was determined that the center value of the threshold variation was to be placed between the sixth and seventh average inputs. Then the distance from the center to the closest extreme was measured and divided into three equal parts to specify the threshold step. The resulting threshold levels utilizing equal steps above and below the center threshold are shown in Fig. 2.

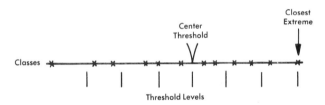

Figure 2. Threshold levels.

LOSS FUNCTION

Many forms of the loss function are possible—polynominal, linear, integral, exponential, and combinations. The time-varying threshold logic design technique is based on an exponential loss function. The loss function serves three purposes: (a) it provides a means for weighting the sample patterns so that the logic units generated are directed towards the remaining difficulties in the problem; (b) it provides a means for assigning output weights to the logic units (the weights assigned minimize the sample loss function); and (c) it provides a means for adding units sequentially by generating a number of candidate units for inclusion in a partially designed machine and selecting the one which gives the greatest improvement in the sample loss function.

For the kth output unit, the sample loss function is

$$L(k) = \sum_i e^{-\xi_i(k)(D_i(k)-\theta(k))}$$

where

$$\xi_i(k) = \begin{cases} 1 \text{ if it is desired that the } kth \text{ decision} \\ \quad \text{unit be activated by the } ith \text{ pattern} \\ -1 \text{ otherwise.} \end{cases}$$

$D_i(k)$ is the total input to the *kth* decision element for the *ith* pattern.

and

$\theta(k)$ is the threshold of the *kth* decision element, selected to minimize $L(k)$.

For the ith pattern, a loss is defined as the sum of its contribution to all of the output unit loss functions

$$L_i = \sum_k e^{-\xi_i(k)(D_i(k)-\theta(k))}$$

The system loss is thus

$$L = \sum_i L_i = \sum_k L(k) = \sum_{ki} e^{-\xi_i(k)(D_i(k)-\theta(k))}$$

OUTPUT WEIGHTS

The time-varying threshold logic unit divides the set of patterns into a number of subsets and allows the relative translation of the discriminant values for these subsets of patterns with respect to the response unit threshold for each output unit. (Since the loss function is additive, it can be minimized by minimizing separately for each output unit. In the following discussion, the kth output unit will be considered.) These subsets are illustrated in Fig. 3. Subset 1 is that set of patterns for which the logic unit does not fire. Subset 2 is that set of patterns for which the logic unit fires at the last threshold, and so forth.

There exists an optimum threshold for the dichotomization of each of these subsets, as determined by optimization of the separability function over the subset. The weights are determined to superimpose these dichotomizing thresholds. Thus, the optimum threshold for Subset 1 is chosen to maximize the separability, S_1,

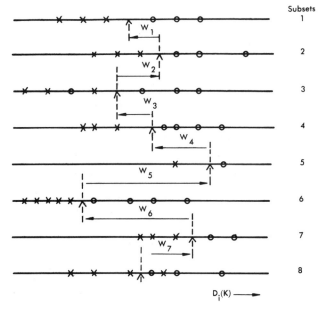

Figure 3. Sample action of time-varying threshold logic.

$$S_1(k) = -\sum_{i\epsilon S_1} e^{-\partial_i(k)(D_i(k)-\theta(k))}$$

and is given by:

$$\theta_1(k) = \tfrac{1}{2} \ln \frac{\sum\limits_{i\epsilon S_1^-} e^{D_i(k)}}{\sum\limits_{i\epsilon S_1^+} e^{-D_i(k)}}$$

where θ_1 is the threshold for Subset 1, and

S_1^- is the subset of patterns of the negative class in subset of patterns S_1

S_1^+ is the subset of S_1 of the positive class.

Therefore the weight for threshold j is

$$W_j = \tfrac{1}{2} \ln \left\{ \frac{\sum\limits_{i\epsilon S^-_j} e^{D_i(k)}}{\sum\limits_{i\epsilon S^+_j} e^{-D_i(k)}} \frac{\sum\limits_{i\epsilon S^+_{j-1}} e^{-D_i(k)}}{\sum\limits_{i\epsilon S^-_{j-1}} e^{D_i(k)}} \right\}$$

COMPUTER PROGRAM

The design for the alphabetic character recognition problem was accomplished on an IBM 7094. The computer program was written in FORTRAN II. It consists of a main program and six subroutines.

The main program (MPM) is an executive routine that inputs the data, calls subroutines to perform separate calculations, and outputs the program results. The input data to the program specifies the activity pattern of the retina cells for each alphabetic character. The selection of logic units starts with the computation of pattern weights (losses). Next, a random number generating library routine is used to determine the connections from the logic units to the retina. Subroutine EARLE is called to compute the input weights and the activity of the logic units. EARLE uses subroutine OSCAR and two library routines to calculate the eigenvectors and eigenvalues needed in computing the input weights. In addition, EARLE calls subroutine SEX to determine the threshold levels. The main program then calls subroutine DAVE to compute the logic unit output weights and the loss functions. Finally, subroutine DIANE redetermines the pattern weights.

Twenty logic units are generated in this manner before the best one is selected for inclusion in the machine. After a unit is selected, two iterations

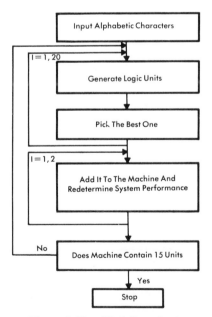

Figure 4. Simplified flow chart.

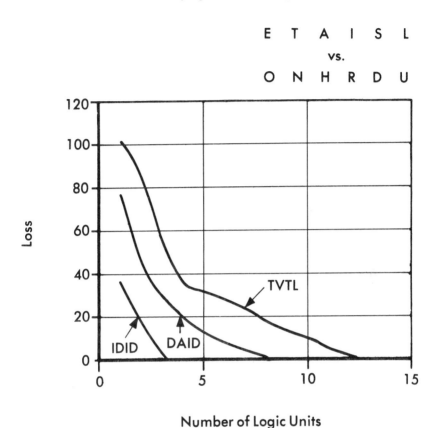

Figure 5. Comparison of designs on pattern separation number 1.

on subroutines DAVE and DIANE are performed to reevaluate the machine and respecify the pattern weights and logic unit output weights. Then subroutine SAM is called to tabulate the machine errors for print-out. In this project, a 15 logic unit pattern recognition device was designed by this technique.

A simplified flow chart of the computer operation is shown in Fig. 4.

PROGRAM RESULTS

The results of this design procedure have been compared with other techniques in order to evaluate the efficiency of time-varying threshold logic. One previous design (IDID) has been tried using linear logic units and iterative design (numerical design, and iterative minimum loss selection) on both the input and output levels. Another design (DAID)

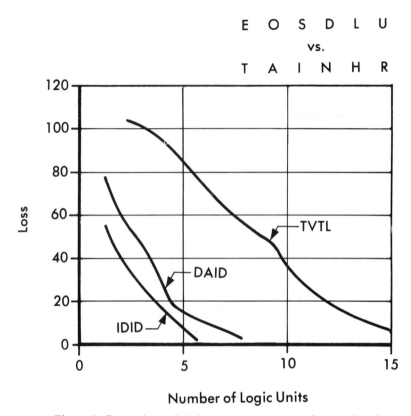

Figure 6. Comparison of designs on pattern separation number 2.

involves linear logic units with discriminant analysis used to specify fixed threshold units and iterative design to approximate the decision hyperplane.[3]

A comparison of the time-varying threshold logic design with these other two designs is complicated by the fact that in both the IDID and DAID designs the problem of recognizing the 12 sets of letters was split in four sections that were designed independently. Each of these sections separates the 12 letters into equal positive and negative classes, and therefore the four designs must be combined to recognize individual letters. The time-varying threshold logic machine was designed with four response units simultaneously, and because of the pattern weighting procedure, devotes most of its attention to the hardest parts of the problem.

Consideration of these differences in the design procedures illuminates the results shown in Figs. 5 through 8. These figures plot the loss function vs. number of logic units. In Figs. 5 and 6, IDID and DAID seem to out-

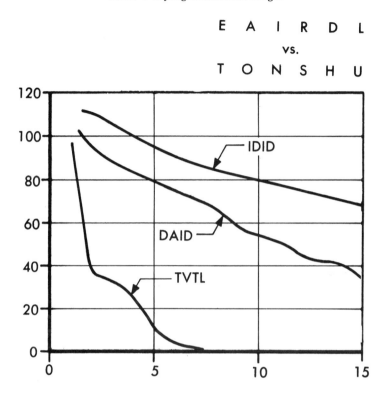

Number of Logic Units

Figure 7. Comparison of designs on pattern separation number 3.

perform TVTL because TVTL is neglecting these easier discriminations as it concentrates on the harder ones of Figs. 7 and 8. On these more difficult separations IDID and DAID make little progress.

Some comparison of the overall performance of the three design techniques can be gained from an analysis of Fig. 9. The four individually designed sections of the IDID and DAID machines were combined for comparison with TVTL. It can be seen that the IDID machine had reached its best performance (minimum loss) with about 32 units. With 30 units, the DAID machine had equaled the performance of the IDID machine and showed signs that the losses could be decreased by adding more units. It can be seen that the 15-unit TVTL machine has about one-seventh the loss of the 54-unit DAID device.

Comparison of the DAID design technique with conventional forced

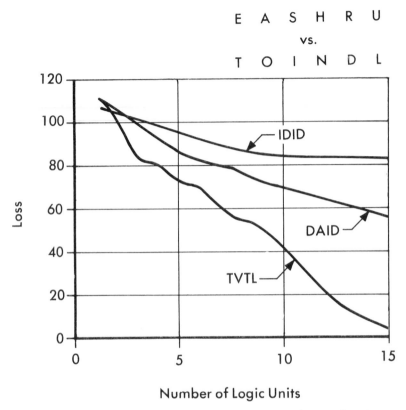

E   A   S   H   R   U

vs.

T   O   I   N   D   L

Figure 8. Comparison of designs on pattern separation number 4.

learning and Bayes-weighting perceptions has been made in previous studies. The results indicate that DAID is at least an order of magnitude better with respect to machine size for a specified error rate.

CONCLUSIONS

The main points of this pattern recognition technique are that a new logic unit and design procedure have been used. The logic unit utilizes a time-varying threshold so that the time the unit turns on is determined directly by the input state. The design employs a discriminant analysis technique to specify the logic units, a heuristic rule for evaluating performance, and an iterative procedure for selecting the best machine. An attempt was made to compare this type of system to other designs. However, a valid comparison can only be made in terms of the cost required to solve a particular problem.

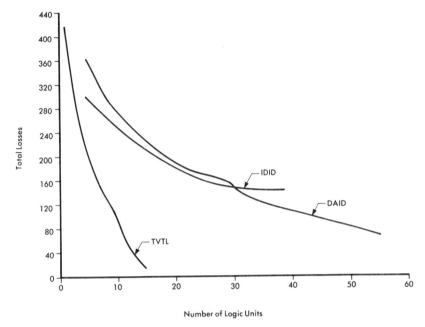

Figure 9. Comparison of complete systems.

REFERENCES

1. R. O. Winder, "Some Recent Papers in Threshold Logic," *Proc. IRE,* Vol. 49, No. 6, June 1961.
2. C. R. Rao, *Advanced Statistical Methods in Biometric Research,* John Wiley and Sons, Inc., New York, 1952.
3. DAID has been shown to be considerably better than the forced learning procedure in perceptrons for similar problems. See Daly, J. A., Joseph, R. D., and Ramsey, D. M., "An Iterative Design Technique for Pattern Classification Logic," *WESCON,* August 1963.

13

A MODULAR SELF-ORGANIZING SYSTEM

R. H. Asendorf

Senior Member, Technical Staff
Theoretical Studies Department
Hughes Research Laboratories
Malibu, California

INTRODUCTION

GENERAL REMARKS

This paper gives a preliminary account of one phase of the research in self-organizing systems which is currently in progress. This work is part of a much broader research program, embracing pattern recognition, statistical decision theory, and the informational sciences in general.* More specifically, within the framework of the present program are such overlapping areas as semantic organization of data (pattern recognition) and intelligent manipulation of information (artificial intelligence).

For the purpose of investigating self organizing systems, the construction of a small, low cost, flexible, modular, special purpose computer of unconventional design was undertaken. It was required that the design be such that the system should be capable of being expanded in size and sophistication into a more advanced machine. Furthermore, the logical design should be easily modifiable in order to simulate various models of self-organizing systems, including adaptive stochastic networks.

---

* Conducted by the Theoretical Studies Department of the Hughes Research Laboratories.

115

The present account will be principally descriptive; no detailed analytical discussion will be presented here.

A broad class of self-organizing systems may be regarded as consisting of three somewhat distinct subsystems or *fields*: an input field, an association field, and an output or response field. In a parallel organized machine the input consists of numerous sensory input channels (a mosaic of photocells, for example). The association area, or middle region, consists of many redundantly interconnected adaptive logic elements, typically a switching circuit with an adjustable response threshold. The output portion of the machine (like the association area) is composed of adaptive logical elements. The output and input portions of the machine are not really essentially different from the association area; their elements are merely specialized forms of association elements.

The adaptive behavior of the system derives from an overall modification of the responses of the individual logical elements.[1][2] This is essentially a feedback network which may be under the control of either a human observer or an auxiliary computer; these comprise the self-organizing system.

MULTIVAC

The machine, which has been designated Multivac *(Multi-V*ariant *A*daptive *C*omputer), consists of a small, high-speed unconventional digital computer which uses solid state printed circuit modules. The machine accepts inputs from a very large number of sensors in a parallel fashion. The sensory field is sampled statistically in a pseudorandom manner. Data is processed sequentially at a clock frequency of 1 mc. The present model of the machine, designated Mark I has 100 binary inputs, 8,190 threshold logic elements, and four output channels. Modular circuitry, using standard diode transistor logic (DTL), is used throughout.

Etched circuits on glass-impregnated epoxy cards are utilized for all logic modules[3]; up to four *flip flops* or eight gating circuits are contained on one card. The logical voltage levels are (0, −6) V. All inputs are diode coupled for isolation, and all output signals are clamped; noise rejection margins are ± 1.5 V maximum. The logic modules use one basic transistor throughout all gating and *flip flop* circuits. Connectors to the cards are of a hermaphroditic type with spring contact and self-wiping action.

A fully compatible logic module family of printed circuit cards provides great logic freedom with a minimum of interconnections (for this purpose taper pin connections are used exclusively). The number of logic inputs is expandable by means of auxiliary diode clusters. (All inputs are expandable to at least 10.) Trailing edge triggering of *flip flops* via ac inputs permits reliable output gating of the input without intervening delay circuits.

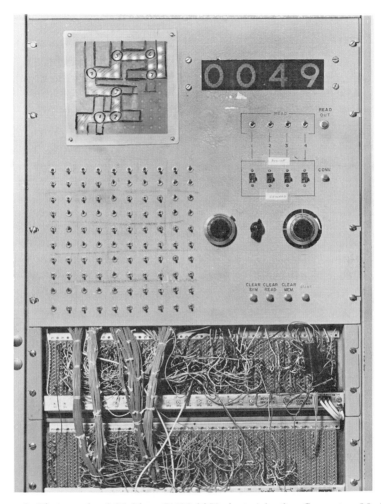

Figure 1. Photograph of Multivac I (Multi-Variant Adaptive Computer, Mark I), a self-organizing system.

The Mark I model includes 58 *flip flops*, 96 active *nand* gates, and 124 passive diode *and/or* gates. In addition, a large number of prewired diodes are used to augment *fan in*. There are over 200 transistors and over 1,200 diodes in the present system.

MODEL EVALUATION

Various approaches for the construction of a self-organizing system were considered; some of these are listed below:

- Optical techniques (with/without fiber optics) [4]
- Multiple-aperture magnetic devices (BIAX, MAD, etc.) [5, 6]
- Chemical cells (Memmisters, Soliens, etc.) [6]
- Conventional transistor diode technology [7]
- Other solid-state techniques (Hall effect, ferro electricity, etc.) [8]
- Other (storage tubes, colloidal association memories, etc.)

The systems can be further characterized as being parallel, sequential or mixed. It is with respect to the association field that the question of parallel versus sequential is most vital.

It was decided to employ diode transistor logic (DTL) in a 1 mc system with parallel inputs, a sequential association field, and quasi parallel output. It was believed that this conventional approach offered the greatest versatility, reliability, and ease of construction, at a modest cost. Furthermore, a high speed, all electronic system would provide a greater degree of compatibility (less of an interface problem) with commercial and military systems. Since this was to be a research tool to study the principles of organizational complexity, it was our desire to be encumbered as little as possible with untried and novel techniques.

In addition, it was felt that an approach which could be microminiaturized (either with present technology or with reasonable projections thereof) would have certain very real advantages; innovations, techniques, and experience gained with the present system might at least have some transfer value to a future microminiaturized system, either commercial or military. Although the desire for microminiaturization was not one of our immediate design objectives (and probably would not even be desirable), the implications for future microminiaturization were considered in formulating our design philosophy.

MARK I AND MARK II

It was planned from the outset that the system should evolve through several recognizable stages of growth, designated as Mark O, Mark I, and Mark II. The Mark I is described in this report. The designation, such as Mark I or Mark II, refers only to some very general characteristics of the machine, and not to any specific form of self-organizing system. The machine designated Mark I or Mark II consists of an ensemble of logical building blocks which can be interconnected to stimulate a perceptron, an artron network, a mixture of both, or neither. Its purpose is to be a scientific tool for the investigation of various theoretical models. For a basis of discussion, however, we shall consider the Mark I in terms of its present interconnections.

A SELF-ORGANIZING SYSTEM

SENSORY FIELD

The sensory field of the Mark I machine consists of 100 digital sensory units, which in the present machine are simple toggle switches. The next version of the machine will have a considerably larger sensory field.

The sensory field is sampled in a pseudorandom manner; some fraction of the sensory field is interrogated every microsecond. This is accomplished by gating the output of each sensory unit with a random signal, which is generated by a pseudorandom pattern generator. Randomized connections between the sensory field and the association field are established in this manner. Deterministic connectivity can also be generated, should this be desired.

PSEUDORANDOM PATTERN GENERATOR[9]

The input channels are scanned by a digital pseudorandom pattern generator which generates a pseudorandom sequence of zeros and ones. This is realized by a conventional shift register with several feedback loops which are linked at nodes, each node being a mod. 2 adder (Fig. 2). For

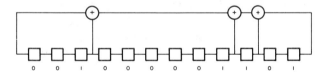

Figure 2. Pseudorandom pattern generator used to generate a random connectivity pattern.

a shift register of n stages, one speaks of n feedback coefficients; the ith feedback coefficient is 1 if a feedback path channel originates at the output of the ith stage, and is zero otherwise:

$$\text{feedback coefficient} = \begin{cases} + \ 1 \text{ if feedback connection,} \\ \ \ \ 0 \text{ no feedback path.} \end{cases}$$

The feedback coefficients may be regarded as the coefficients of a certain polynomial. The feedback generates a *recursion* relationship, and gives rise to a polynomial domain. With a proper choice of feedback coefficients, an invariant space is generated which is irreducible over the polynomial ring. Said differently, the polynomial domain has no divisors, and consequently the shift generator is forced to run through the entire domain of the polynomial (i.e., to generate all possible sequences of zeros and ones). At any one instant there will be a unique digital pattern in the shift register. The patterns generated in this way are all distinct and will not repeat until the major cycle of $2^n - 1$ clock pulses has been completed.

If the feedback coefficients had been chosen differently, to correspond to a reducible polynomial, the period of the shift register would be sub-maximal (less than $2^n - 1$). In the present system $n = 12$; correspondingly, the cycle is 4,095 clock pulses long.

ASSOCIATION FIELD AND INHIBITORY CONNECTIONS

In the present machine there are two association cells which exist in real time; consequently, during a complete machine cycle of 4,095 μsec, a system of $2 \times 4,095 = 8,190$ association cells is simulated.

There are numerous pathways which connect the sensory field with the rest of the system. A particular pathway may be either purely excitory in character, or purely inhibitory, or possibly of a mixed character. These various types are indeed present in Multivac. However, it will simplify the present discussion to regard a given pathway as being either purely excitory or inhibitory in character.

Inhibitory connections play an important role in all self-organizing systems. While it is possible to construct simple models that function with a complete absence of inhibitory connections, such connections are of utmost importance for systems of even moderate complexity. Many of the simple control commands in the program of a conventional digital computer take the form of inhibitory statements. The real value of an inhibitory control channel is that it provides an opportunity of interacting with other signal carrying channels.

In the present system the number of inhibitory pathways is a variable number which is under the direct control of the operator. When the number of inhibitory pathways is made to assume its minimum value, the system behaves as if there were no inhibitory connections. As the number of inhibitory connections is increased, more and more inhibitory channels are activated. Generally the number of inhibitory connections is regarded as a fixed parameter and is not usually varied during the course of an experiment. The situation in the existing system is actually more complicated than the simple description just given; however, it represents the qualitative behavior reasonably well. Because of the manner in which the inhibitory connections are utilized, the logic performed by the association field is not simply linear threshold logic. The association field is, in fact, a multi-layered association field, of which some elements are linear threshold elements, while others are not.

The only nonstandard building blocks in the system are the threshold logic gates which make up the association field. The threshold logic gates of the Mark I have 10 digital inputs, an adjustable (analog) threshold, and a single digital output. The digital inputs are summed and compared with a reference threshold θ_0; if the threshold θ_0 is exceeded, the cell fires (output is a logical one); if the threshold is not exceeded, the cell fails to fire (and the output remains a logical zero).

The threshold action is provided by a voltage-sensitive gate; this is performed by a tunnel diode which subsequently switches a transistor.[10] A tunnel diode serves as an excellent switching element by virtue of its bistable switching characteristic. Furthermore, the tunnel diode, when used in level detection, has considerable advantages over the conventional Schmitt trigger: (a) high speed (switches in picoseconds); (b) sharply defined threshold; (c) small amount of energy required to effect switching (estimated to be about $10^{-15}J$; for example, the energy to switch a transistor is typically $10^{-9}J$); (d) greater stability.

The switching threshold of the tunnel diode threshold detector (TDTD) is controlled by the setting of a potentiometer in the circuit. The parameter which determines the firing of the association cell (or TDTD) can be expressed by specifying either the potentiometer setting θ_0, or by $\theta_0(n)$, the number of active inputs required to activate the cell. Figure 3 shows that

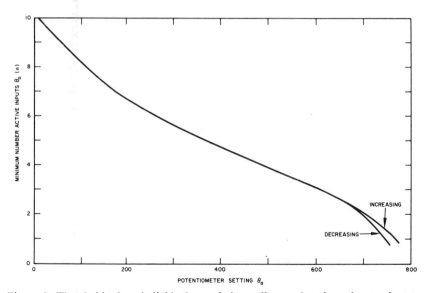

Figure 3. Threshold of an individual association cell as a function of potentiometer setting θ_0. The minimum number of active inputs required for firing is denoted by $\theta_0(n)$. Note the slight hysteresis at the lower end.

θ_0 and $\theta_0(n)$ are related almost linearly and without any appreciable hysteresis (except for the very lowest part of the curve). The data presented in this figure was [sic] taken under dynamic operating conditions, i.e., the input channels were being scanned at a 1 mc rate (once every microsecond). It will be noted that a potentiometer setting of $\theta_0 = 372$ corresponds to majority logic (i.e, $\theta_0(n) = 50\%$).

It should be emphasized that when the excitory threshold θ_ϵ is changed, all excitory cells of the association layer are modified en masse; in anthropomorphic terms, this is rather analogous to the adaption of the human eye to the ambient light level.

MEMORY AND THE RESPONSE FIELD

The memory is a recirculating magnetostrictive delay line having a delay of 4,095 μsec. A delay of 4,095 μsec. at 1' mc corresponds to a storage capacity of 4,095 bits. This type of memory storage was chosen because of its speed (1 mc), reliability, and low cost. The Mark II system will employ a magnetic drum for long term storage and will retain the recirculating delay line for short term storage.

Each response unit gives a direct numerical readout of the number of active A cells connected to it. The present system has four response (output) channels; additional response channels could be provided without difficulty if desired. Literally hundreds of thousands of possible pathways exist between the input sensory field and the final output channels. The *connections* between the association field and the response field are simulated. For each A to R connection there is associated in the memory either a logical one (connection exists) or a logical zero (no connection exists). Therefore, for a given threshold, the memory contains an enumeration or listing of the various pathways which are active in the system. Since the recirculating memory and the pseudorandom number generator have identical periods, they operate synchronously; the random number generator generates the S to A connections and the memory simulates the A to R connections. No difficulty has been experienced with this synchronous mode of operation.

MASKS, PARALLEL AND SEQUENTIAL

As stated earlier, the sensory field is sampled in Monte Carlo fashion, 8,190 times; this can be restated in the following more highly intuitive and suggestive manner. It may be considered that the system generates a fixed ensemble of 8,190 random *masks*. A necessary condition that the ith sensory unit may transmit during the mth sampling interval is that the mth random sampling mask have a hole corresponding to the ith sensory unit, and in addition, only if the ith sensor is firing. In real time, the output of the association field is a time sequential one dimensional pattern which represents the input signal or message, having been encoded by the threshold detectors and by the logic of the association field. It is frequently convenient to refer to this encoded signal as the *stimulus mask*. This is a single one dimensional time independent *mask,* while the random sampling masks are an ensemble of two dimensional masks which exist in parallel, e.g., one complete mask every clock pulse. This masking concept is useful because it facilitates the discussion of reward/punishment. It is to be emphasized that reward/punishment affects the contents of the memory; in fact, the only way that information can enter the memory is via the reward/punishment control circuits. * Furthermore, the reward/punishment commands are issued only in coincidence with the appropriate stimulus masks. In this manner we ensure that only those A cells which are firing *incorrectly* are punished, and that only *deserving* cells are rewarded (e.g., for a given stimulus, the system searches among its A cells, and selects out a fraction of those A cells which are not connected to the output, but which, if they were connected, would strengthen the desired response). The logic that accomplishes this is done sequentially and merely involves a simple comparison with a portion of the stimulus mask. Herein lies the utility of the concept of the stimulus mask. In this manner, a fractional part of stimulus can be entered directly into the memory. The control, however, resides completely with the reward/punish circuitry, as stated above.

It should be emphasized that the memory system just described is essentially an associative (or content-addressed) memory. Perhaps *semantically organized* memory describes the situation better. Although the operation of the present system is sequential, it is clear that a parallel mode of operation is actually being simulated. In any case, the use of the masking concept, the manner of addressing, and the manner of interrogation are characteristic of an associative memory.

REWARD/PUNISH

Two highly specialized inputs, called reward and punishment channels, are associated with every output response channel. Under the control of either a human operator or an auxiliary computer, the reward and punishment channels can be activated to provide a controlled amount of feedback,

---

* There are two exceptions to this rule. For some situations it is convenient to be able to inject a random signal into the memory; in addition, for diagnostic purposes, injection of a logical "one" in each of the 4,095 memory locations is sometimes desirable.

thereby modifying the response of the system for a given stimulus. Favorable pathways through the system are thereby strengthened (rewarded) while others are weakened (punished). Actually, the invoking of reward and punishment consists of selectively modifying the contents of the memory. If a given output channel has too many active pathways which feed it, it is possible for a number of these connections to be removed (i.e., somewhere in the memory, *ones* are replaced by *zeros*). Similarly, the response of a particular output channel can be strengthened by making new connections (somewhere in the memory, certain *zeros* are selectively replaced by *ones*). In this way the internal configuration or *state* of the system is modified. The reward or punishment options are established by the setting of several three-position switches (punish, reward, and neutral), one for each output channel. These options are not applied until a special *convergence* button is activated. Then, for some fraction $f(\tau)$ of the total frame time (4,095 μsec), the reward/punish options are applied. The severity of the reward/punishment is controlled simply by altering the length of reward/punish interval. It is possible, for example, to punish severely and reward lightly (or not at all); to reward heavily and punish lightly, etc. In this manner we can achieve a very flexible strategy for reward and punishment.

ELEMENTARY BEHAVIOR

The Mark I system has been trained to discriminate alphanumeric symbols, to play *tic tac toe,* and even to *run a maze.* We wish to emphasize that the system was not specifically designed to perform any one specialized task. The only things that distinguish these various situations are (a) the training received, and (b) the manner in which the inputs and outputs are interpreted. We present below a brief account of a few representative experiments. This will illustrate some of the operational modes of the system.

THRESHOLD SEPARATION

Using one output channel and all available A cells, the present system is capable of unambiguously recognizing all $26 + 10 = 36$ alphanumerics, provided that the symbols are of standard font and that the presentation is restricted always to the same area of the sensory field. (This latter restriction can be removed, and it is then possible to demonstrate the system's ability to generalize; this is discussed separately below.) For this purpose, it is convenient, but not necessary to use a pseudorandom sequence of "zeros" and "ones" in the memory as the starting engram (memory trace).

Each alphanumeric symbol evokes a different response in the association field, and presents a characteristic numerical readout (eigenvalue) associated with that pattern. Those stimuli which give responses that are identical, or are not well separated, can be easily separated by invoking reward/ punishment control; experience indicates that in most cases this affects the already well separated patterns only slightly. It should be emphasized that two different patterns that evoke the same numerical readout nevertheless excite distinctly different patterns in the association field. The probability that two different stimuli excite identical states in the A-field can be shown to be negligibly small.

Discrimination is effected in the following manner; let σ_i be the ith a *priori* stimulus, and let θ be the ith a priori response. Let the θ_i be arranged in a monotonic sequence, which is labeled by the index k. Now given that the response is r_μ, what is the probability that the stimulus was σ_i? The answer to this question is given by the conditional probability $p\ (\sigma_i|r_\mu)$. We now make the following ad hoc assignments:

$$p\ (\dot{\sigma}_i|r_\mu)\ =\ 1 \quad \text{if.}\tfrac{1}{2}\ (\theta_i^{k-1} + \theta_i^{k})\ < r_\mu <\ \tfrac{1}{2}\ (\theta_i^{k} + \theta_i^{k+1})$$
$$= 0 \quad \text{otherwise.}$$

This merely expresses somewhat formally a simple intuitive equidistant partitioning of the Hamming distance between two adjacent classes. [11] Table I gives the learned response to 26 alphabetic symbols (excitory threshold $\ell_E = 640.00$). It is easily seen that the separation is not dependent simply on the number of sensory units that are excited. This point cannot be emphasized too strongly.

It should be pointed out that the separation of standard alphanumeric characters can be effected without the use of any inhibitory connections whatsoever. Moreover, separation can be effected over a wide range of excitory thresholds. However, the detailed manner in which the system responds is very much a function of the system parameters.* For example, given a particular state of the system, the machine may give similar readings for both the letters *I* and *J,* but widely different values for *I* and *S*. We express this by saying that the machine confuses *I* and *J,* but does not confuse *I* and *S*. However, simply by changing the system parameters, it is possible to find a new response of the system which reverses this situation, i.e., now *I* and *S* are confused, while *I* and *J* are separated. Of course, in either state the system is amenable to subsequent reward/punish commands to effect further separation.

---

* Excitory threshold and number of inhibitory connections.

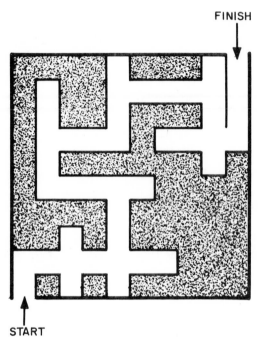

Figure 4. The maze

MAZE RUNNING

The maze shown in Fig. 4 was used to investigate the ability of the system to learn to traverse an arbitrary maze. For the purposes of this problem the four output channels were considered to be labeled North, South, East, and West. The maze is run by successively turning on additional lights. Whenever a decision is required, the four output channels are interrogated. The strongest response from a particular channel (North, South, East or West) determines the direction of the next move. Having been guided through the maze successfully once, it is not guaranteed that the system will traverse the maze successfully on the next attempt; the learning that takes place near the end of the maze may interfere with that acquired near the beginning of the maze.

If a decision is required only at branching points, only seven correct decisions are required to negotiate the maze successfully. This can be easily learned in three or four runs. However, if a correct decision is required at each step along the way, then 29 correct decisions are required, with the system deciding from among North, South, East, or West at every step. The machine can learn this after an additional five or six runs. The number of learning experiences required to learn traversing the maze depends very considerably upon the strategy used. If one attempts to train the system step by step along an unfamiliar maze, the learning progresses very slowly. However, if the system is first *broken in* by training it at the branching points, then the overall learning time is considerably reduced.

Once the maze has been negotiated point by point, then clearly it is possible to remove all the (fictitious) partitions or walls that constitute the maze; the system still traverses a path through the fictitious maze; this is equivalent to the execution of a terrain avoidance course.

TABLE 1
Learned Response to 26 Alphabetic Symbols

Symbol	Sensory Units	Response
I	6	003
S	16	008
Y	9	018
P	16	053
D	18	069
Q	18	083
V	11	108
L	11	117
J	9	163
N	16	257
T	10	304
R	18	337
Z	16	367
A	20	417
W	16	450
C	14	474
U	14	487
F	15	497
E	20	512
K	13	664
G	17	753
B	21	788
O	16	797
H	16	848
M	16	883
X	12	919

STATISTICAL SEPARABILITY AND CONDITIONAL PROBABILITY

Consider the problem of effecting a statistical separation between two symbols, for instance, E and F. For this purpose we arbitrarily choose any two of the response units, and decree that one will be the response unit for E and the other will be the response unit for F. (It may be desired to train the system beginning with a random sequence of digits, although this is by no means necessary.) Using the reward channel exclusively, the E channel can be made to respond strongly to E and, similarly, the F channel to F. These responses may be thought of as being unnormalized conditional probabilities.

Given that the stimulus is E, what is the unnormalized probability that the eth response unit (correctly) identifies the stimulus as belonging to the eth target category? Denote this by $N(e|E)$.

Given that the stimulus is F, what is the unnormalized probability that the fth response unit (correctly) identifies the stimulus as belonging to the fth target category? Denote this by $N(f|F)$.

Given that the stimulus is E, what is the unnormalized probability that the fth response unit (incorrectly) identifies the stimulus as belonging to the fth target category? Denote this by $N(f|E)$.

Given that the stimulus is F, what is the unnormalized probability that the eth response unit (incorrectly) identifies the stimulus as belonging to the eth target category? Denote this by $N(e|F)$.

As a result of the rewarding of eth and fth channels, the numerical values of $N(e|E)$ and $N(f|F)$ will be quite large. However, $N(e|F)$ and $N(f|E)$ may also be large; this would indicate considerable overlap in the projection of E and F upon the association field. This overlap can be arbitrarily small (reduced to zero) by the use of the punishment channel. With F on the sensory field, the quantity $N(e|F)$ can be brought to zero by applying punishment to the eth channel. Similarly the fth channel can be corrected. The total response for the *pure states* $N(e|E)$ and $N(f|F)$ is now less than before (this is a necessary consequence of the removal of overlap). However, the final response is still quite respectable (a typical value for a pure state such as $N(e|E)$ might be $N(e|E) = 160$), and now there is no longer any interaction between E and F.

It was tacitly assumed in the foregoing that the presentation of E and F is always of the same size and at the same place on the sensory field. If the symbols are allowed to be presented at arbitrary locations on the sensory field, this requires the system to generalize. This represents a problem of greater difficulty and sophistication than before. It can still be handled in the following manner. One can no longer insist that all overlap be reduced to zero, but can merely require only that the one correct response unit dominate over the others. A typical learning curve is shown in Fig 5. The oscillating behavior is typical; this type of data is [*sic*] frequently displayed as an average over many dozens of trials, in which case the curve becomes smooth.

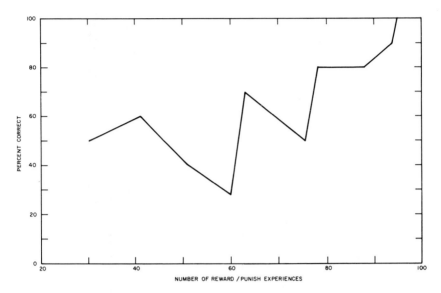

Figure 5. Learning curve for generalization of E versus F. Each test point represents ten interrogations.

REFERENCES

1. A. Corneretto, "Electronics Learns from Biology," *Electronic Design,* Vol. 8, No. 19, 38 (September 14, 1960).

———"Advanced Concepts Studied for Pattern Recognition," *Electronic Design,* Vol. 9, No. 5, 28 (March 1, 1961).

———"Bionics: Rising Interest Fosters Growth," *Electronic Design,* Vol. 11, No. 8, 4 (April 21, 1963).

———"Learning Machines: How Much Progress?" *Electronic Design,* Vol. 11, No. 24, 36 (November 22, 1963).

2. M. R. Uffelman, "Conflex I, A Conditioned Reflex System," *IRE International Convention Record,* Vol. 10, Part 4, 132 (1962).

3. Purchased from Computer Control Corporation.

4. J. A. Ogle and J. M. Kurtzberg, "A Distributed-Network Processor," Proceedings, 1964 National Conference, p. 39.

———"Fiber-Optic Array Recognizers Audio Patterns," *Electronics,* 35, 28 (October 26, 1962).

5. Y. Chu, *Digital Computer Design Fundamentals,* McGraw-Hill, New York, 1964, Chapter 8.

H. S. Crafts, "Components That Can Learn," *Electronics,* 36, 49 (March 22, 1963).

6. *Self-Organizing Systems,* 1962, Spartan Books, Washington, D. C., 1962, p. 435.
   R. N. Lane and D. B. Cameron, "Current Integration with Solien Liquid Diodes," *Electronics,* 32, 53 (February 27, 1959).
7. W. A. Saver, "How to Achieve Majority and Threshold Logic with Semiconductors," *Electronics,* 36, 25 (November 29, 1963).
8. D. Gabor, W. P. L. Wilby, R. Woodcock, "A Universal Non-Linear Filter, Predictor and Simulator which Optimizes Itself by a Learning Process," *Proc. IEE, 108B,* 422 (1961).
9. B. Elspas, "The Theory of Autonomous Linear Sequential Networks," *IRE Trans., CT-6,* 45 (1959).
   W. W. Peterson, *Error-Correcting Codes,* Wiley, New York, 1961.
10. *Tunnel Diode Manual,* General Electric, 1961 (First Edition), p. 43f.
    D. S. Cleverly, "How to Design a Tunnel-Diode Threshold Detector," *Electronic Design,* Vol. 11, No. 19, 58 (September 13, 1963).
    P. J. Langlois, "Tunnel Diodes Boost TRL Speed," *Electronics,* 36, 50 (May 10, 1963).
11. R. W. Hamming, *Bell Sys. Tech. J.,* 29, 147 (1950), *Bell Labs Record,* 28, 193 (1950).

14

ARTIFICIAL INTELLIGENCE THROUGH A SIMULATION OF EVOLUTION*

LAWRENCE J. FOGEL, ALVIN J. OWENS and MICHAEL J. WALSH

General Dynamics/Astronautics, San Diego, California

INTRODUCTION

Both the bionic and heuristic programming approaches toward artificial intelligence attempt to model the information processing characteristics of that intelligent creature—Man. The immense complexity of the central nervous system, coupled with our incomplete knowledge of the neural and molecular mechanisms, limits our ability to replicate the biological entity which provides human intellect. Networks of threshold elements may simulate arrays of neurons, but this is a far cry from providing behavior at higher levels of abstraction. In short, the case for replicating nature in terms of physical correspondence stands on weak ground (as witness the fact that modern aircraft are not ornithoptors).†

Taking a broader view, heuristic programming focuses attention upon psychological aspects of human decision making in an attempt to devise logic which will overcome specific problems in a manner similar to that of an intelligent man. A variety of game playing and theorem proving programs have been successfully demonstrated, but this mimicry falls short of

---

* This research was in part supported by the Office of Naval Research (contract Nonr 4539 (00)) and in part by Goddard Space Flight Center, NASA (contract NAS 5-3907).

† These comments should not be taken as an attack on bionics. Such modeling may well provide valuable insight into biophysical functioning.

providing the flexibility which is essential to intelligent behavior; nor does it furnish an insight into the fundamental logic which makes intellect possible. Success in the field of artificial intelligence should require that inanimate machines solve problems which still remain to be solved by man, not because of their sheer speed, accuracy, or greater memory, but because they discover new techniques for solving the problem at hand.

Still another approach toward artificial intelligence is possible. Man may be recognized to be but a single artifact of the natural experiment called evolution; an experiment which has rather consistently produced creatures at higher and higher levels of intelligence. Might it not be far wiser to model the process of evolution—iterative mutation and selection—in order to discover successively better logic for seeking the given goal under the constraint imposed by the environment?

Intelligent behavior can result from an ability to predict the environment coupled with the selection of an algorithm which permits the translation of each prediction into a suitable response. For the sake of clarity, the following discussion will primarily be concerned with the problem of predicting the behavior of the observed environment. More specifically, the problem at each point in time is to devise an algorithm which will operate on the sequence of symbols thus far observed in order to produce an output symbol which will agree with the next symbol to emerge from the environment. Simulated evolution provides a means towards this end.

DISCUSSION

An arbitrary finite-state machine is exposed to the sequence of symbols which have thus far emerged from the environment. As this occurs, each output symbol from the machine is compared with the next input symbol. The percent correct score is a measure of the ability of this machine to predict the already experienced environment on the basis of the preceding symbols. An *offspring* of this machine is then produced through mutation, that is, through a single modification of the *parent* machine in accordance with some mutation noise distribution. Thus the offspring is made to differ from its parent either in an output symbol,* a state-transition, the number of states, or the initial state. †

---

* In the case of a binary environment, a deterministic procedure can be used to replace this type of mutation. As each symbol from the environment is predicted on the basis of the preceding symbols score is maintained of the relative frequency of success of each state-transition. A predictive fit score of greater than 0.5 can then be ensured by the reversal of output symbols on those state-transitions which were *more often wrong than right.*

† That state the machine is in when it receives the first symbol of its experience.

The offspring is now exposed to the same sequence of symbols which were experienced by the parent-machine and its prediction capability is similarly scored. If this score is found to equal or exceed that of the parent, the offspring survives to become the new parent. If not, it is discarded and a new offspring is generated. In this manner nonregressive evolution proceeds through successive finite-state machines which individually evidence increased ability to predict the already experienced sequence of symbols. At any point in time the remaining machine can be used for actual prediction; that is, it can be exercised by the last symbol to emerge from the environment thus producing an actual prediction of the next symbol to be experienced. The same machine is then used to parent succeeding offspring which are evaluated over the now longer recall. Thus the evolution continues in fast time in preparation for the next required actual prediction. Such predictions may take place periodically, aperiodically, or on request. They may be made whenever a specified predictive fit score has been attained, when some prechosen number of offspring have been evaluated, or when an appropriate number of generations* have occurred. Of course, in general, the longer the time interval between successive predictions, the greater the expectation of success. Similarly, the greater the speed of the computer facility (increase in the number of evaluated offspring) or the larger the available memory (increase of their permissible size) the greater the evolutionary prediction capability.

The evolutionary technique offers distinct versatility. For example, the desire to predict each second symbol in the future can be satisfied simply by scoring each offspring in terms of the correspondence between its output symbols and those symbols which emerge from the environment two symbols later. By the same token, appropriate scoring of the offspring permits the prediction of any particular future symbol, the average of some set of future symbols, or indeed, any well-defined function over the future. The desire for minimum error prediction may be satisfied by using a *magnitude of the difference* error matrix. Minimum *rms* error prediction results if each term of this error matrix is squared. If "a miss is as good as a mile" the error matrix should have equal nonzero off-diagonal terms and zero on the diagonal.

But, the purpose of the simulated evolution need not be restricted to prediction in any sense. The input symbols of the evolving machines may be individually associated with the set of possible stimuli, the output symbols with the set of alternative response, the goal: to achieve any well-defined function over the future sequence of responses. Here there is no longer a distinction between prediction and the algorithm which translates

---

* Defined later in this section.

prediction into response. The evolutionary program recommends each action in the light of its expected overall worth with respect to the given goal.

At the same time, it is reasonable in the interest of economy, to desire that the offspring be of minimum complexity. The maxim of parsimony may be directly incorporated into the evolutionary procedure by reducing the score of each machine in proportion to a measure of its complexity. The amount of this penalty may be influenced by the particular characteristics of the computer facility upon which the simulation is to be carried out. Thus, at each point in time, the evolutionary technique provides a non-regressive search through the domain of finite-state hypotheses for that logic which best satisfies the given goal under the constraint imposed by the available computation capability.

Efficiency of the simulated evolution can be improved in a number of ways. Any available information concerning the underlying logic of the environment can be incorporated in the form of the initial machine. If this *hint* is reasonably correct, the evolution should require fewer generations to attain the same score. If it is incorrect, this introduction of *false* information in no way precludes solution of the problem, although it may be expected to reduce the efficiency of the procedure.

Suitable choice of the mutation noise can increase the efficiency of evolution. For example, an increase in the probability of adding a state generates a wider selection of larger machines which should benefit evolution against a complex environment. In fact, the probability over the modes of mutation can be made to depend upon the evidence acquired within the evolutionary process itself. Thus, an experienced greater relative frequency of success for, say, changing the initial state might be made to increase the probability of this mode of mutation. Although this procedure may benefit the prediction of independent environments, it can offer a danger if the environment is interactive . . . an intelligent adversary might discover the specific dependency and use this knowledge to construct an obverse strategy.

The evolutionary search may be viewed as a selective random walk, a *hill climbing* procedure, in a hyperspace defined to include the finite-state machines and an additional coordinate on which is measured the predictive fit score.* The danger of becoming trapped on a secondary peak can be overcome by permitting multiple mutation, with the multiplicity being a function of the difference in predictive-fit score of successive generations. Thus, as the search nears a peak greater and greater *attention* is devoted

---

* The term "predictive-fit" is used in place of the more general "functional-fit" in view of the more immediate concern with the problem of prediction.

to generating more radical offspring in the hope of striking a point which may lie higher on the slope of another peak.

The evolutionary technique may be expected to predict nonstationary environments because of its continual search for a *best* logic. But selection of only the single best logic may be an overly severe policy. Certainly those offspring which have predictive-fit scores also characterize the logic of the environment in some meaningful manner. Why not mimic nature and save the best few machines at each point in time? In general, the highest scoring offspring has the greatest probability of giving rise to an even better offspring, thus it should receive most attention in terms of mutative reproduction. Lower ranked offspring may be regarded as insurance against gross nonstationarity of the environment. The distribution of mutative effort may well be in proportion to the normalized predictive-fit scores. Evaluated offspring are inserted into the rank order table of retained offspring and a generation is said to occur whenever an offspring is found which has a score equal to or greater than the score of the best machine.

All of the retained machines need not lie on the slopes of the peak which is identified by the best machine. Thus, saving the best few offspring may maintain a *cognizance* over several peaks, with the relative search effort being distributed in proportion to the expectation of significant new discoveries. The greater the number of surviving offspring, the larger the number of possible peaks. Of course, saving a greater number of offspring decrease the efficiency against a well-behaved environment. Here again, if properly chosen, the number of retained offspring and the distribution of mutative attention can improve the efficiency of evolution, but, at the same time any such restriction offers a danger if the environment takes the form of an intelligent adversary.

The efficiency of natural evolution is enhanced by the recombination of individuals of opposite sex. By analogy, why not retain worthwhile *traits* which have survived separate evalution ·by combining the best surviving machines through some genetic rule, mutating the product to yield offspring? Note that there is no need to restrict this mating to the two best surviving *individuals*. In fact the most obvious genetic rule, majority logic, only becomes meaningful with the combination of more than two machines[†]. Clearly, this opens the door to many new possibilities. For example, it may be fruitful to explore the combining of the best machines of several different generations in the hope of finding a model of the models

---

† It is always possible to express a finite set of machines which operate through a majority logic element as a single machine. Each state of the majority machine is a composite of a state from each of the given machines. Each transition is described by the input symbol which caused the respective transition in the given machines and by that output symbol which results when majority logic is applied to the output symbols from the given machines.

which had thus far been most successful. It is tempting to speculate on an obvious extension of this procedure which would operate simultaneously at several levels of abstraction, thus recombining the best machines over various levels.

EXPERIMENTS

In the interest of brevity only some of the series of experiments which were conducted to explore the predictive capability of the evolutionary technique will be reported, these being numbered consecutively for ease of reference. The original evolutionary program was written in Fortran II for the IBM-7094 to permit prediction of 2-symbol environments. This set of experiments demonstrated the feasibility of predicting cyclic environments, stationary environments, and the primeness of each next number in the sequence of positive increasing integers. [1,2]

A second program was then written to permit the prediction of 8-symbol environments. Unless otherwise indicated all of the following experiments started with the same arbitrary five-state machine. The recall was permitted to grow with experience starting with 40 symbols before the first prediction. The penalty for complexity was chosen to be 0.01 times the number of states in that machine. Single, double, or triple mutation of each parent machine occurred with equal probability and a maximum of 40 offspring or 10 generations were permitted before each successive actual prediction.

The first set of experiments concerned the prediction of an environment composed of a cyclic signal created by repetition of the simple pattern 13576420 which was disturbed by increasing levels of noise. With the environment consisting only of the undisturbed signal (Experiment 1) the evolutionary technique discovered a perfect one-state predictor machine within the first 18 evaluated offspring. The environment for Experiment 2 was generated by corrupting this signal by the equally-likely addition of $+ 1$ or $- 1$ to certain symbols, these being identified by skipping a number of symbols from the last disturbed symbol in accordance with the next digit drawn from a uniformly distributed random number table. Quite arbitrarily, addition to the symbol 7 and subtraction from the symbol 0 were assumed to leave these symbols undisturbed. Thus, 82.5% of the symbols were left undisturbed. As shown in Fig. 1, 59.3% of the first 81 predictions were correct, there being only 6 errors in the last 30 predictions. During the evolution 3,241 different offspring were evaluated, the predictor machines growing in size to eight states.

The environment of Experiment 3 was obtained by disturbing the environment used in Experiment 2 once again in the same manner. Thus,

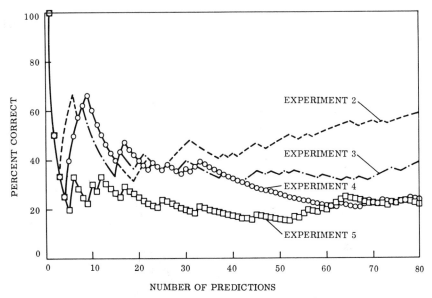

Figure 1. Evolutionary prediction of the environment

28.9% of the symbols were disturbed by ± 1, 1.5% were disturbed by ± 2; leaving 69.6% undisturbed. As shown in Fig. 1, 39.5% of the first 81 predictions were correct, there being a general increase in score in the last 20 predictions. During the evolution 3,236 different offspring were evaluated, the predictor machines growing in size to 15 states.

The environment for Experiment 4 was obtained by disturbing the environment used in Experiment 3 again in the same manner. Thus, 37.0% of the symbols were disturbed by ± 1, 2.5% were disturbed by ± 2, and 0.1% were disturbed by ± 3; leaving 60.4% of the symbols undisturbed. As shown on Fig. 1, 23.5% of the first 81 predictions were correct. During the evolution 3,214 different offspring were evaluated, the predictor machines growing in size rather steadily to 19 states.

The environment of Experiment 5 was obtained by disturbing a randomly chosen 50% of the symbols in the signal. Thus, 43.8% of the symbols were disturbed by ± 1 (the difference being due to the adopted rule concerning addition to 7 and substraction from 0); leaving 56.2% undisturbed. As shown in Fig. 1, 22.2% of the first 81 predictions were correct. During the evolution 3,195 different offspring were evaluted, the predictor machines growing in size somewhat irregularly to 17 states. It would appear that this last increase in the noise level (from 39.67% in Experiment 4 to

43.8% in Experiment 5) resulted in significantly degraded prediction of
the environment for only the short recalls.

Figure 2 indicates the degree of correspondence between the sequence
of predictions and the signal in these experiments. Note that after the
first 76 predictions the signal was predicted in Experiment 5 as well as

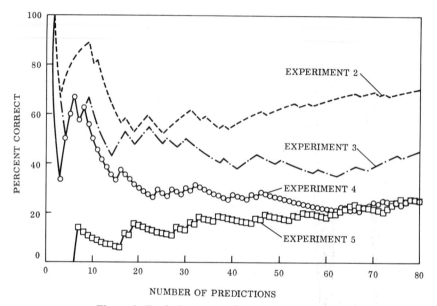

Figure 2. Evolutionary prediction of the signal.

it was in Experiment 4 in spite of the fact that a larger percentage of the
signal symbols had been disturbed. This may be due to the fact that in
the last experiment the symbols remained closer to the original signal.
Such "consideration" for the magnitude of deviations is a result of using a
distance-weighted error matrix, in this case the weighting being the magnitude of the symbol difference. In essence this choice converts the nominal
scale of symbols to an ordinal scale.

It is of interest to examine each of the predictor-machines as representations of the periodic properties of the environment. The characteristic
cycle for any finite-state machine is found by starting it in its initial state
together with the first symbol of the recall then driving it by each of its
successive output symbols until the output sequence is periodic. All of
the characteristic cycles in Experiment 2 were eight symbols in length.
The first 73 corresponded perfectly with the pattern of the signal but this
insight was lost in the later predictions which were in error by one or

two symbols. After the 14th prediction, the characteristic cycle remained 13576430.

The higher noise level of the third experiment resulted in characteristic cycles of varying length until the 26th prediction. From then on until the 70th prediction the characteristic cycle remained 1357643113576430, this being in error one symbol out of every two cycles of the signal. As expected, the result of Experiment 4 was more erratic with the length of characteristic cycle jumping from 8 to 16 and remaining the same after the 73rd prediction. Each of the last 24 characteristic cycles were 62.5% correct. Experiment 5 revealed even greater varability in the characteristic cycles. A majority of these were 8 or 16 symbols in length and reflected the basic pattern of the signal although there was little *one-to-one* correspondence.

The environment for Experiment 6 was generated by disturbing every symbol of the signal by + 1 or − 1 with equal probability. At first glance it is surprising to find the prediction of the signal improved as shown in Fig. 3, but note that with the disturbance of every symbol one aspect of

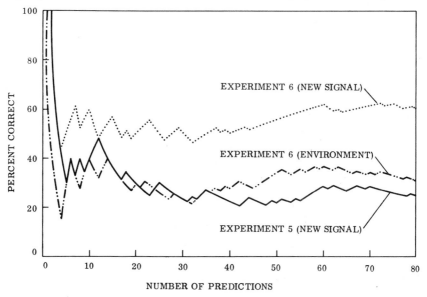

Figure 3. Comparison of Experiments 5 and 6.

the randomness of the environment was removed. In essence the signal had taken on a new form, the boundaries of the original signal 24677531 or 02465310, each having equal probability at each point in time. In the first 81 predictions this new signal was properly identified 70.4% of

the time. In fact, the characteristic cycle of the last predictor-machine was
02267731102665331. This can be seen to lie on the boundaries of the
original signal except for one symbol of every 17. In order to provide a
basis for comparison the percent correct prediction of the environment is
also shown as well as the result of Experiment 5 with respect to the new
signal.

It is natural to inquire as to the extent the prediction capability will be
degraded by *wild noise* (each disturbed symbol being replaced by a randomly chosen symbol from the input alphabet). The environments of Experiments 7 and 8 were generated by imposing this kind of disturbance on
the original signal once and twice, respectively. As expected, the ability
of the evolutionary program to predict the environment, as shown in Fig.
4, was somewhat poorer than in the comparable Experiments 2 and 3.

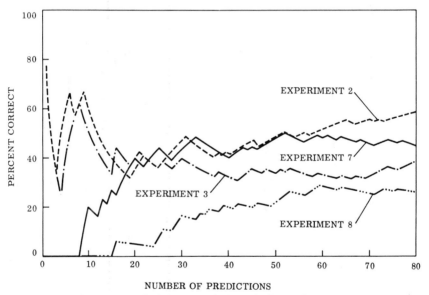

NUMBER OF PREDICTIONS

Figure 4. Evolutionary prediction of the environment.

Figure 5 indicates the degree of correspondence between the sequence of
predictions and the signal in these same experiments. Here again the
additional degree of randomness within the noise degrades the performance.
Carrying this noise to the extreme results in a perfectly random environment. Experiment 9 revealed no significant ability of the evolutionary program to predict this environment.

The introduction of randomness always introduces questions of repeat-
ability. In order to examine this point Experiment 2 was repeated nine

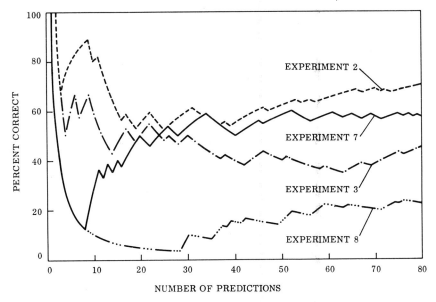

Figure 5. Evolutionary prediction of the signal.

additional times, the results being shown in Fig. 6. As expected, the variability is an inverse function of the score.

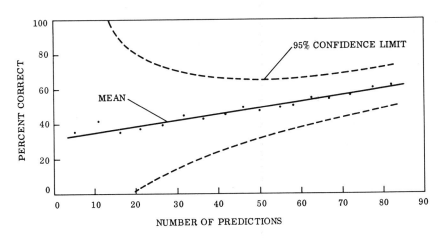

Figure 6. Statistics of Experiment 2.

The second set of experiments were concerned with the prediction of purely stochastic environments. Experiment 10 required the prediction of a zeroth-order four-symbol Markov environment, the arbitrarily chosen probabilities being 0.1, 0.2, 0.3, and 0.4. This information, as prior knowledge, would dictate the continual prediction of the most probable symbol giving the asymptotic score of 40%. At the other extreme, perfectly random prediction would have an expected score of 25%. As shown in Fig. 7

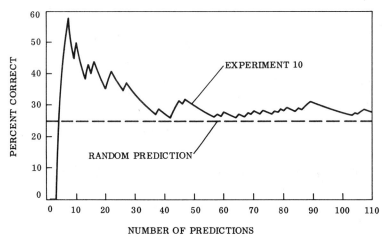

Figure 7. Evolutionary prediction of zeroth-order Markov environment.

the evolutionary score settled between these extremes thus demonstrating the purposeful extraction of information from the previous symbols.

The first order environment of Experiment 11 was generated by the arbitrary transition matrix shown in Table 1. The actual environment had the transition matrix of relative frequencies shown in Table 2.

TABLE 1

Arbitrary transition matrix

	0	1	2	3
0	0	0.8	0.1	0.1
1	0.1	0	0	0.9
2	0.9	0.1	0	0
3	0	0.1	0.8	0.1

TABLE 2

Transition matrix of relative frequencies

	0	1	2	3
0	0	0.822	0.071	0.107
1	0.035	0	0	0.965
2	0.915	0.085	0	0
3	0	0.077	0.862	0.061

The marginal frequencies of this environment were 0.236, 0.241, 0.249 and 0.274, respectively.

With prior knowledge that the process is first order it would be possible to attain the score of 89.5% on the 200th prediction in the manner shown in Fig. 8. *But even without this knowledge the evolutionary prediction*

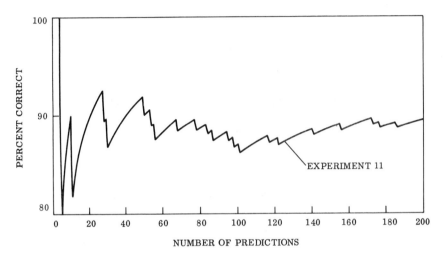

Figure 8. Evolutionary prediction of a first-order Markov environment.

technique attained this same score at each point. Analysis of the sequence of predictions revealed that at the end of this experiment the environment was properly characterized by the maximum transition probabilities of each row. Other experiments were conducted on first and second order processes with similar results.

To generate a more difficult environment, the powers of 2 and 3 were rank-ordered and reduced modulo 8, that is, 1234010300010300100-3010030100300. . . After the first 300 predictions (Experiment 12) the percent correct score reached 88.7. 1,401 different offspring were evaluated using an *all or none* error matrix (all off-diagonal elements have a value of 7 and all main-diagonal elements a value of 0). The predictor machines were generally of six states. In order to avoid the reduction to three symbols in the latter portion of the sequence, the powers of 2 and 3 were rank-ordered and reduced modulo 7 yielding 12341220414254112431122-461424512143122461. . . After the first 216 predictions (Experiment 13), the percent correct score was 56.6, this being found through the evaluation of 3,671 offspring, which were generally of about 21 states. The score for the last 50 predictions was 78%. Certainly the prediction capability was far better than chance would yield. Prediction of this sequence based on the most probable symbol up to each point in time yields a score of only 8.5%.

A set of experiments was conducted in order to evaluate the evolutionary technique as a means for detecting the existence of correlation between variables, this correlation to be used to enhance the sequential prediction of one or more of the sensed variables. In Experiment 14, a random sequence of binary symbols were presented to an arbitrarily chosen finite-state machine, M (shown in Table 3). Note that four different symbols comprise the output alphabet of this machine. The evolutionary program was required to predict each next symbol in the output sequence, this being predictable only to the extent that the structure of the machine M is superimposed upon the otherwise random driving signal. The percent correct score, shown in Fig. 9, reveals increasing stability as the score settles around 51% after the first 152 predictions (with 20 symbols as the initial recall).

TABLE 3. Machine M

Present State	Input Symbol	Next State	Output Symbol	Present State	Input Symbol	Next State	Output Symbol
1	0	3	2	3	1	4	1
1	1	5	0	4	0	5	3
2	0	1	2	4	1	3	0
2	1	2	3	5	0	2	0
3	0	1	1	5	1	1	2

This prediction score should be considerably improved if the program were permitted to evolve finite-state representations on the basis of both the 4-symbol output sequence and the 2-symbol input sequence. In fact, with this additional information, the prediction score should asymptotically approach 100% as the recall increases in view of the deterministic nature of machine M. Experiment 15 was conducted to investigate whether or not this would take place through the evolutionary technique. At each point in time two-input single-output finite-state machines were evaluated in terms of their predictive-fit of the known recall of the 4-symbol output sequence while driven by the preceding recall of both the 4-symbol and 2-symbol sequences. The percent correct score, shown in Fig. 9, attains a value of 80%.

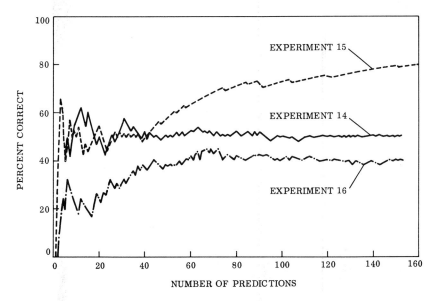

Figure 9. Evolutionary prediction of the 4-symbol environment.

In some sense, the sequence of evolved double-input single-output machines should provide an increasingly accurate representation of the transduction performed by machine M. Figure 10 is a graphical representation for the finite-state machine which evolved after 160 predictions. This machine, N, has the states designated by letters in order to avoid any confusion with the number-designated states of machine M. It is possible to compare machine N to machine M in the following way: examine each state of M in order to determine if there is some state in machine N which in some sense will perform the same function when given the same sequence of input symbols. (Note that the input to each state of machine N consists of an ordered pair of symbols, the first being the input to the state machine M and the second being the previous output of machine M before it entered that state.)

To illustrate, consider state 1 of machine M. Since the outputs of the transitions which enter this state are either 1 or 2, the possible corresponding inputs to machine M are 0, 1; 0, 2; and 1, 2. Examination of state B of machine N shows that 0, 1 and 0, 2 both yield the output symbol 2 which corresponds to the output of state 1 when it receives an input symbol of 0. Similarly 1, 1 and 1, 2 produce an output of 0 which corresponds to the output of state 1 when it receives input symbol 1. Similarly, 1, 1

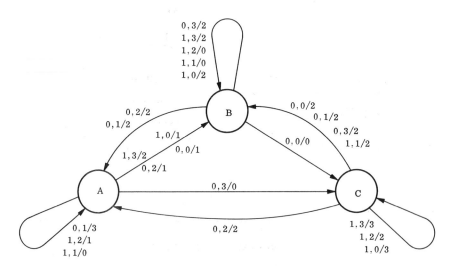

Figure 10. Machine N.

and 1, 2 produce output symbol 0 which corresponds to the output of state 1 when it receives an input symbol 1. Thus, state 1 of machine M may be said to be contained in state B of machine N in the sense that machine N will yield the same response if given a corresponding sequence of inputs. Following this logic it can be shown that state 3 is contained in state A and state 5 is contained in state B.

Viewing the problem in the large, it is often essential to erect hypotheses concerning the logical relation between two or more separately sensed variables. It would appear that the evolutionary technique offers a means for finding multiple input predictor machines which can be translated into reasonable representations for the observed logical relationship.

Experiment 16 was conducted to confirm the claim that the evolutionary technique had, indeed, extracted useful information from the correlative input variable in Experiment 15. In Experiment 16 two-input single-output machines were evolved in the very same manner as before but in this case the binary variable which was offered was uncorrelated with the output sequence taken from M in that it was independently generated. The percent correct score, shown in Fig. 9 remains below the corresponding scores which resulted from the previous two experiments. In other words, the additional information which was furnished in the form of an independent binary variable formed a *distraction* resulting in poorer predictive-fit and predictions. More specifically, the more complex machines which were considered made successful mutation and selection less likely.

In view of the apparent need, a formal technique was devised which permits expression of the set of finite-state machines which are functionally contained within any given machine. Thus it becomes possible to translate each predictor machine into a set of hypotheses concerning the transduction logic of the environment. The finite-state machines which are functionally contained in the set of machines used for successive prediction can be examined for consistency which may be expected to provide additional insight.

*   *   *

It is of interest to consider some of the ways in which the evolutionary technique is similar to and different from other approaches to the problem of artificial intelligence. It might be argued that the evolutionary program is to some extent like a *linear threshold device* in that each finite-state machine can be represented in terms of a network of threshold elements. True, but in general such a network requires more complex logic than that of a linear threshold device. A linear threshold device which has no internal feedback is representable as a *one state* machine. The evolutionary technique develops multi-state machines as required.

It might be argued that the evolutionary technique is a *heuristic program* on the grounds that it is in essence "reasonable." It is indeed reasonable, but it was not written in an attempt to simulate the logical behavior displayed by the human decision maker.

An essential aspect of intelligent behavior is versatility. In contrast to the statistical decision procedures which operate well only within the restricted domain of stationary environments, the evolutionary technique has been applied with considerable success over a wide range of goal functions and environments. This technique utilizes the available evidence at each point in time, making only one assumption concerning the mature of the environment: that the logic which would have best satisfied the goal within the remembered experience is that logic which should be used for the present decision. In general, the fewer the assumptions, the greater the versatility.

The evolutionary technique is more closely related to some of the iterative *function-fitting techniques* of modern mathematics. These are almost always restricted to the consideration of point functions rather than transduction functions as represented by finite-state machines. The evolutionary search technique is therefore carried out in the meaningful domain of possible decision makers which affect a causal universe.

Of course, a final choice among alternative methods to enhance or replace human decision making must rest on economic grounds. Thus far the evolutionary program remains experimental, the primary concern here being feasibility. A comparative economic evaluation will be carried out later in this program of research.

CONCLUSIONS

The key to artificial intelligence lies in automating an inductive process which will generate useful hypotheses concerning the logic which underlies the experienced environment. The creatures of natural evolution are just such hypotheses, survival being the measure of success. As described above, some fundamental aspects of this process can be replicated with finite state machines proceeding through iterative mutation and selection in order to find a *best* logic to satisfy the given goal in the light of the available memory of experience. Real-time decisions can then be based upon the extracted results of this continuing fast-time evolution.

A series of experiments were conducted in order to evaluate this concept. An 8-symbol language evolutionary program was given the goal of predicting a variety of time-series on the basis of the previous symbols. These *environments* consisted of a cyclic signal embedded in various kinds and amounts of noise, purely stochastic environments which contain the signal only in the form of the transition matrix, nonstationary samples of deterministic sequences, and multivariate sequences which were the input and output of an arbitrary transduction. In every case, the results attained compared favorably to those which would be expected from conventional techniques using only the same information. It was, in fact, possible to identify some of the cyclic and stochastic properties of the signals from the predictor machines.

The success of these experiments demonstrates that useful models of the regularity within a sequence of observation can, indeed, be found by the evolutionary technique. Although this demonstration was restricted to a variety of goals relevant to prediction there would appear to be no need to maintain this constraint. So long as the correctness of each response can be evaluated prior to the next response, the goal may be made to reflect the immediate concern of the decision maker.

The first phase of computer technology was devoted to the development of equipment which would carry out a large number of simple operations quickly and reliably. The second phase of computer technology was devoted to the development of languages which permit the detailed instruction of this equipment in an efficient manner. Computer technology is now entering a new phase in which it will no longer be necessary to specify exactly how the problem is to be solved. In contrast it will only be necessary to provide an exact statement of the problem in terms of *goal* and *costs* in order to allow the evolution of the best program possible within the available computation capability. Solution of the problem then includes a statement of the discovered algorithm. The old saw "the computer never knows more than the programmer" is simply no longer true.

The scientific method consists of *induction,* inductive inference, followed by independent verification. Hypotheses, generated so that they cover the available evidence and additional data points, are individually evaluated in terms of the validity of their inference. Those that prove worthy are modified, extended, or combined to form new hypotheses which carry on a "heredity of reasonableness." As the hypotheses correspond more and more closely with the logic of the environment they provide an "understanding" which can be used for the improvement of goal-seeking behavior in the face of that environment.

The correspondence between natural evolution and the scientific method is obvious. Individual organisms in nature serve as hypotheses concerning the logical properties of their environment. Their behavior is then an inductive inference concerning some as-yet-unknown aspects of their environment. Their health is a measure of their suitability. Their offspring include the heredity of reasonableness as well as additional information resulting from mutation and recombination.

The evolutionary technique described above is then a realization of the scientific method in which the hypotheses are restricted only in the sense that they be finite-state machines. The creation of successive hypotheses requires the introduction of randomness as well as the prevailing logic of inheritance. The versatility which is essential to intellect is a natural product of the iteration. In essence, the scientific method is an essential part of nature. It is no wonder, then, that its overt exercise has provided mankind with distinct benefits and now permits even its own automation through the artificial evolution of automata.

REFERENCES

1. L. J. Fogel, A. J. Owens and J. Walsh, "On the Evolution of Artificial Intelligence," *Proceedings of the Fifth National Symposium on Human Factors in Electronics, IEEE,* San Diego, May 5-6, pp. 63-76.
2. L. J. Fogel, A. J. Owens and J. Walsh, "An Evolutionary Prediction Technique," presented before International Conference on Microwaves, Circuit Theory, and Information Theory, *IEEE,* Tokyo, Japan, September 7-11, 1964. Summary published in Part 3 of the *Proceedings,* pp. 173-174.

COMMENTS AND REPLIES

GOLD* *(Stanford):* Fogel reports having used, as input in his *evolution simulator,* the characteristic function of the set of prime numbers, *P(t),* defined on the positive integers to be

$$P(t) = 1 \text{ if } t \text{ is prime}$$
$$0 \text{ if } t \text{ is not prime}$$

As he noted, *P(t)* can be generated by no inputless finite automation (their output functions are necessarily ultimately periodic). However, $P(t)$ is a primitive recursive function, and it is of interest to note that an evolution simulator which tries primitive recursive functions, rather than being restricted to the functions produced by inputless finite automata, would eventually identify $P(t)$ correctly.

This is the content of the proof of Theorem 7 (actually, its application to Corollary 7) of my paper titled "Limiting Recursion." * To see this, observe that the goal of Fogel's evolution simulator, if it is presented with a nonprobabilistic function of time, is what I call *identification of a function in the limit.* In order to construct an evolution simulator which will identify any primitive recursive function in the limit, the key point to note is that the class of primitive recursive functions is effectively enumerable. That is, it is possible to order the primitive recursive functions,

$$p_1(t), p_2(t) \ldots p_a(t) \ldots$$

with repetitions, in such a way that there is a single algorithm which will compute $p_a(t)$ for any given values of a and t. It is only necessary for the evolution simulator to do the following: at time t it considers the first t primitive recursive functions of the enumeration and chooses that one which best agrees with the inputs received so far. It is important that the enumeration be effective so that the evolution simulator can have the capability computing any desired value of any specified primitive recursive function.

Fogel's evolution simulator is very similar to Friedberg's computer program which he calls *Harvey.*[†]

FOGEL: I appreciate the remarks of Gold concerning primitive recursive functions. *Harvey* was one of a number of programs (Herman, Sherman, Sampson, Homer, Teddy, Ramsey, et al.) written by Friedberg, et al., to automatically formulate sets of instructions which might solve certain simple problems. These programs differed from one another in their

---

* E. Mark Gold, "Limiting Recursion," to appear in the *Journal of Symbolic Logic.*
† R. M. Friedberg, "A Learning Machine," *IBM Journal of Research and Development, 2,* 2-13 (1958) and *3,* 282-287 (1959).

erations to cope more effectively with new environments that
1 some of the problems their ancestors had faced before.

I appreciate Hormann's suggested experiment. Although this
experiment has not yet been conducted, it is reasonable to expect
machines which evolve under goal *A* will initially increase in com-
when the goal is changed to goal *B*. Gradually these machines
ce complexity in order to more efficiently satisfy goal *B*, this at
cit cost to goal *A*. Eventually, the inheritance of *learned aspect*
1 will disappear. Of course, the more similar the goals, the greater
fer of training and the less the increase in complexity. In fact,
ease in complexity may furnish a measure for the dissimilarity of
1 goals. These remarks are based upon experiments in which the
nained invariant but the environment was suddenly and radically

(Northrop Nortronics): Fogel's paper at this symposium exposed
s work for the first time and I am not sure that I fully absorbed
ications of the evolutionary approach to artificial intelligence. But
rs to me that the comments made during the discussion session at
posium to the effect that the evolution scheme possesses many
of a learning scheme, are valid. Nor need this view detract from the
ishments presented, for surely much remains to be done in con-
; models of learning and Fogel's approach is distinct and novel
experimental results invite attention.

ttedly, the finite state machines which are replicated and mutated
he evolutionary process do not themselves learn. The learning is
d by the master computer program. Thus, one could argue that
nary *learning* which requires discarding many *organisms* is difficult
ify with learning by individual organisms which do not discard
. of themselves. But as the title of the paper indicates, Fogel fully
to identify the evolutionary process with artificial intelligence
s a property usually associated with individuals, not generations.
more, the master computer program does not discard any organisms
'sical sense, it only discards, or better said, re-organizes those parts
computer and program which comprise the organism. Viewed in
nner the program appears an excellent and novel approach to a
; or self organizing system.

1 emphasizes the prediction aspect of intelligence and, unless I
taken, includes such functions as detection, discrimination and
recognition as subordinate to and serving the function of prediction.

specific heuristics but generally relied upon the
with which each instruction on record is active de
it is performing currently and partly on its long-
experimental results demonstrated significant di:
while programs by such means. In his summary, Fi
we should go from here is not entirely clear." In
ments failed because of a lack of sufficient logic
of a single instruction causes a radical change
single mutation of a finite-state machine does
character.

HORMANN *(System Development Corp.):* It woul
how Fogel's *evolving organisms* would do in the fc

> Suppose that an offspring α has been produ
> *A* successfully, and that α has gone through
> tionary processes, producing its offspring
> generations down) to achieve goal *B*. Is β li
> of the characteristics of its ancestor α. Th
> offspring β do when presented with goal *A*
> goal *A* immediately, or would it have to go
> process again as if it had been presented
> How would the degree and aspects of simil
> *A* and goal *B* affect the process?

If we consider the *evolving organism* as one in
the *mutation process* as an aspect of adaptatioi
questions seem to imply the presence of *transfer c*
that is, either positive or negative effects of pre
learning.

But there are, perhaps, other inferences that m
questions. Fogel stressed that the new offspring
specified goal would not necessarily be more compl
of states) than its ancestor, unless the particular gc
more complexity. This would be considered a good
ment of the organism were always restricted to one g
However, it seems reasonable to assume that th
adaptive an organism were, the richer in problems it
(That is, the environment could contain a greatei
situations; some of these problems might never b
ganism.)   In the light of this consideration, in
descendants and retention of some of the *ancestoi*
be a desirable feature. Such complexity and trait-

new g
contair

FOGEL
specific
that the
plexity
will re
an imp
of goal
the *tra*
this in
success
goal re
change

KLEYN
me to
the im
it appe
the sy
aspect:
accom
structi
and hi

Ad
during
exhibi
evolut
to ide
portio
intend
which
Furth
in a p
of the
this m
learni

Fos
am m
patter

It is interesting to cast pattern recognition proper into a prediction model. Pattern recognition poses the problem of discovering the *many-to-one* mapping which associates categories with a set of inputs. These categories are the ones into which a human perceiver maps the inputs. In the case of pattern recognition through learning the problem is to construct a machine which discovers this mapping for itself. What information does such a machine have to go on? Just the input sets and some symbols or special names which the human perceiver uses to designate the input sets. From this viewpoint, the task of the machine is to predict the response of the environment, which here is the human perceiver, to the input sets which both are exposed to. It remains to be seen if there is an advantage in viewing the problem in this manner.

FOGEL: With respect to Kleyn's commentary, it is well to note that the learning does take place by the evolutionary program and not by the individual *organisms*. Clearly the program is Darwinian and not Lamarckian. This is not to say that individual learning could not be added to the procedure. The results of research in this direction will form the basis for a future paper.

Again, let me remark that prediction was used as a means for the identification of the existence of signal in noise (detection) and for the representation of that signal in terms of reflection of the finite-state predictor-machine (discrimination). If reference signals are available, these may be predicted to yield predictor-machine representations which may be individually compared to the evolved predictor-machines in order to permit pattern recognition. But the goal need not be restricted to prediction. It may well be generalized to allow the direct evaluation of the worth of each model in terms of the worth of its sequence of previous responses. In such a case, control decision-making is accomplished with prediction becoming an identified intervening variable. Let me emphasize that prediction is but a particular goal which serves the purpose of demonstration.

OVERTON *(North American Autonetics Div.):* A ubiquitous problem regarding research concerns the translation of results into terms which other scientists and the general public can understand. Such translation is obviously necessary if the results of research are to be adequately exploited; by definition, the specialist doing the research is not intimately conversant with the many practical problems to which the results might conceivably be applied. Furthermore, it is obviously impossible for one researcher to compare his work with that of another if he does not understand the other's concepts and terminology. This situation—the existence of personal concepts which have been expressed in language made up by a researcher for his own use—exists to an appreciable extent in the cybernetic sciences.

Fogel has contributed to an amelioration of this situation with his paper, "Artificial Intelligence Through the Simulation of Evolution." By describing what some of us are doing in new terms and with different analogies, he has helped us to look at our research in a different light.

The above statements, of course, represent a personal reaction to his paper. I know Fogel feels the specific details of his work are more significant. But, given the fact that he obviously knows more than I do about what he is doing, it is my opinion that his translation is the more valuable contribution.

Among the particularly interesting analogies which one may draw from his translation are these:

- The state of a learning program after one "pass through a lesson"* is analogous to a mutated system (in this case, a machine) after one generation;
- The analysis of the nature of the lesson is analogous to the degree of prediction that the environment will permit some system to reach;
- Most basically, there is an analogy between learning and evolution.

Among the results of this way of looking at learning machine work are these ideas:

- The retaining of tentative memory of the results of the last few passes through the lesson would seem to be profitable because it is analogous to keeping the few best systems after a period of mutation;
- It may be well to add size or cost of memory to the evaluation criteria because of the analogy with the efficiency with which an animal uses its food;
- It is possible that the statistics applicable to genetic behavior might be found to include techniques which would be useful in analyzing the possible results of the combination, or *mating* of systems of learning.

FOGEL: Overton's commentary deserves clarification and correction. I am happy if the evolutionary approach to artificial intelligence provides a new

---

* This jargon is used at Autonetics

vantage point from which it is possible to review other research in this field. In general, the analogies cited are valid, but I would like to add a few discriminating remarks.

- A *generation* occurs when an offspring is identified which demonstrates a better score with respect to the given goal over the available recall than the best score of the retained machines. The learning of the evolutionary program may proceed even without the passage of generations. These just mark significant points of success. The program may be made to *pass through a lesson* more than once using the last evolved machine as a hint in that it serves as the original machine for the next review of the lesson.

- The evolutionary program may be used for prediction, interdiction or post-diction. Prediction was chosen only as a means to demonstrate the capability of the evolutionary technique. A *lesson* should only be characterized in terms of its predictability if this happens to be the goal to be achieved.

- Indeed, evolution does provide learning at the *specie* level rather than at the level of the individual.

The resulting *ideas* may be stated as follows:

- Inheritance of the best few theories is always good practice. Here the term *best* only becomes meaningful if the goal is well-defined so that each hypothesis may be tested. The mutative construction of new models should always continue (in the case of the evolutionary program, the theories, hypotheses, models, conjectures, representations—call it what you will—took the form of finite-state machines);

- Cost is always an important factor in data processing. The demand for realism requires that cost minimization be a part of the goal to be achieved;

- It is felt that worthwhile rules for the combination of off-spring may arise from studies of genetic coding or from pure mathematical as well as from statistical analysis of natural evolution.

15

SEARCH BY EVOLUTION*

H. J. BREMERMANN, M. ROGSON and S. SALAFF
University of California at Berkeley

1. INTRODUCTION

Long before man discovered computers, there have been biological data processing systems. Among these are the central nervous system, hormonal control systems and the genetic system. The latter copies, transmits, mutates, mates and selects genotypes.

The idea to stimulate biological evolution in order to evolve optimal structures, programs (for example, for pattern recognition), heuristics (for example, in game playing), etc., has been suggested or tried by a number of authors: Friedberg,[1] Samuel,[2] Fogel, Owens, and Walsh,[3] and Bremermann.[4, 5]

Friedberg tried to evolve short computer programs through *mutation* and *selection of the fittest*. He found that sometimes the desired program did not evolve at all and sometimes evolution took longer than pure chance or longer than a straightforward program of systematic search through all possible cases would have taken.[1]

Minski[6] also has reported disappointing results with *hill climbing* schemes which are related to evolution. In contrast, Fogel, in his paper in

---

* This research was supported by the office of Naval Research on contracts NONR 222(85) and NONR 3656(08).

Although this paper was not part of the formal program of the Symposium, it is included in the Proceedings because of its direct relevance to the subject matter of other papers and because it was discussed in some detail at the Analysis and Review Sessions. [ED.]

these proceedings, reports success in evolving *finite-state automata* that are selected according to their efficiency in predicting the available history. Further, Samuel's checkers playing program, in adjusting weights of its evaluation function, employs an evolutionary method. Samuel's program is perhaps the most successful game playing program thus far developed.

Our work has produced both schemes that converge very well and programs that are very *resistant* to convergence. In the early work programs tended to stagnate far from the optimum and refused to converge no matter what seemingly reasonable modifications and tricks were tried. A detailed description of these experiments may be found in Bremermann and Salaff.[7] Later work took a different approach and many of the problems that did not converge before were easily solved by the new method (Bremermann-Rogson [8]).

An understanding of the phenomenon of stagnation of an evolution process should be of basic interest. As was pointed out by Fogel in his talk at this conference, and by Bremermann[4], evolution is a widespread phenomenon: technologies, machines, systems, social organizations, etc., evolve. These development processes have features that are similar to biological evolution. As efforts are being made to develop new knowledge, products, and technologies through research, it should be of interest to realize that an evolutionary process can stagnate far from an optimum under one scheme while it progresses efficiently under another.

2. LINEAR SYSTEMS

While most other authors who have worked with evolutionary techniques have been concerned with complex problems for which algorithmic methods are missing, we choose to study the evolution of solutions to simple problems. Only when the problem is well understood is it possible to assess exactly how well the method is doing.

In the early work we tried to solve systems of linear equations through evolution, using the following approach: Given an $n \times n$ matrix $A = [a_{ij}]$ with non-vanishing determinant, and with b and x defined as *n-tuples* of real numbers, we define $R(x)$ as,

$$R(x) = \sum_{i=1}^{n} (\sum_{i=1}^{n} a_{ij}x_j - b_i)^2$$

A solution, $x^{(o)}$, of the system is obtained if $R(x^{(o)}) = O$. Since det $A \dagger O$ the solution is unique. The hypersurface $y = R(x)$ in the $n + 1$ dimensional Euclidean space is convex (no local extrema other than $x^{(o)}$).

The given initial *try* x is perturbed by adding an increment, Δx. By the obvious analogy such perturbations are called *mutations*. There is, however, a significant difference: the components of x vary over a continuum, while genes vary over a finite number of alleles. The continuous perturbations may be quantized by choosing the components $\Delta x_i = -c$, O, or $+c$, where c is a constant (in some cases c is multiplied by a random factor which is uniformly distributed over an interval).

It is reasonable to expect that by a continued process of mutation and *selection of the fittest one* would approach the solution vector $x^{(o)}$. Mutation: replacement of x by $x + \Delta x$. Selection: select each $x + \Delta x$ to take the place of x if $R(x + \Delta x) < R(x)$, otherwise retain x).

It is easy to see that the process would converge if one could search through all possible directions. If we quantize by choosing $\Delta x_i = c$, $-c$ or O, where c is a constant, then there are 3^n possible directions. For n small, say $n < 5$, this is not a serious problem; however, the number of possible directions increases exponentially. For $n = 10$ the search task already becomes formidable, and for $n > 30$ it becomes practically impossible.

Biological evolution faces the same problem. At the level of genes there are at least $2^{10,000}$ genotypes, and if the possible nucleotide sequences are considered, there are many more. Even with large populations and millions of years it is not possible to evaluate all these possible genotypes by trying out each of the corresponding organisms.

Evolution, instead, mutates each gene with a certain probability. Most often one gene is mutated at a time. Very rarely are there more than three or four simultaneous mutations. In addition mating creates new genotypes through combination.

Simulating biological evolution, one component Δx_i was changed at a time. Initially, *mating was not included*. Unfortunately, this method stagnates at a point far from the solution. At such a *point of stagnation* further progress is possible only if several *genes* are changed simultaneously. In one case, six out of 10 variables x_i had to be changed simultaneously (six non-zero components of Δx) in order to have $R(x + \Delta x) < R(x)$.

Suppose that at a stagnation point m genes have to be changed. Since, in general, it is not known which ones have to be changed, all possible m-tuples out of n have to be searched. There are $\binom{n}{m} = \dfrac{n!}{(n-m)!\,m!}$ such m-tuples. For $m = \dfrac{n}{2}$ we have, by Stirling's formula, $\dfrac{n}{m} \approx 2^n$. For anything but small n (say $n < 30$) this is a forbiddingly large number.

Nature seems to overcome such stagnation points by mating. Various mating schemes were tried: intermediate inheritance (taking the arithmetic mean of two difference approximations), as well as several dominant-recessive schemes. None of these schemes (tried on linear systems) brought much improvement. Also, several variations of the basic method of asexual evolution described above were tried: different discretizations, different mutation probabilities, and integer problems with binary coding of the integers and mutation on the bits. A more detailed description of these experiments may be found in Bremermann-Salaff[7].

The phenomenon of stagnation was so persistent that one may ask whether many biological species are similarly "hung up" at a stagnation point. Perhaps *ecological niches* have to be interpreted as stagnation points rather than optimal adaptations. Such a point *looks optimal* for all single gene mutations, multiple gene mutations being so rare and their resultant possibilities so plentiful that the occurrence of the right change has so low a probability that no such occurrence can be expected in earthly times and populations. Changes in the environment (geological transformations, ice ages, breakthroughs in other species) may be important factors in keeping biological evolution in a state of flux.

In the course of our experiments it was learned that the *condition number* of the matrix (a_{ij}) plays an important role. The condition number is the ratio of the largest to the smallest eigenvalue of (a_{ij}). For condition numbers close to 1 near convergence was eventually obtained for up to 30 variables. However, for condition numbers larger than 5 the method stagnated even for a small number of variables. The experiments were programmed in Fortran; the computer was an IBM 7090. Table 1 summarizes these experiments; n is the number of variables, P the condition number, T the time taken in seconds, R the remaining "residue." Rather than the residue described in equation (1) we have used (mainly for reasons of

$$\text{simpler computability } R = \sum_{i=1}^{n} \left| \sum_{j=1}^{m} a_{ij} x_j - b_i \right|. \tag{2}$$

TABLE 1

Residue (R) for Various Condition Numbers (P),
Number of Variables (n), and Times (T)

n	P	T	R
12	2.09	10.9	0.00075
20	2.05	20.0	0.000092
30	2.0	61.8	0.00098

A case of n=50, P≈2 was also tried. It had not converged after two minutes and the case was terminated in order to conserve computer time.

The dependence on the condition number is summarized in Table 2. All cases listed are for $n=5$ and the experiments were terminated after 1.2 sec. The right column lists the residue; in these experiments,

$$R=\sum_{i=1}^{n} \ (\sum_{j=1}^{n} \ a_{ij} \ x_j - b_i)^2 \qquad (3)$$

TABLE 2

Dependence on Condition Number: Asexual Evolution

P	R
3	.001
5	.011
7	.014
7.5	.023
8	.098
8.5	.14
9	9.8
11	5.8

Some of the reasons responsible for stagnation were analyzed by Bremermann and Salaff.[7] In brief, the program hangs up at a *ridge*. It also becomes apparent why mating (taking arithmetic means) in general could not be expected to be very helpful. It appeared that in the latter respect linear programming problems would be more promising.[9]

3. LINEAR PROGRAMMING

In linear programming problems the task is to find that point of a convex polyhedron that is closest to a hyperplane. In the following we refer to this hyperplane as the *cost plane*. (There may be several points closest to the cost plane, but in most cases of interest the solution is unique). The problem is nearly trivial for a small number of variables but nontrivial if the number of variables is large. For example, if a polyhedron is given by 200 inequalities in 100 variables, then the number of different intersections of 100 constraint planes is 2^{200}, and each of these points is a potential candidate for the solution. (G. Dantzig's widely used simplex method is able to solve linear programming problems involving as many as 1000 variables).

Initially we proceeded as follows. From an initial point, $x^{(0)}$, in the convex polyhedron we randomly chose directions and proceeded in these directions (or their opposites) until the boundary of the polyhedron is reached. In this way a *population* of points on the boundary is generated. Then a subfamily of points closest to the *cost plane* is selected and averaged (mated) in order to provide a point to replace $x^{(0)}$. Then the cycle is repeated. Several variations of this basic scheme were also tried, including the method of mutating points on the boundary of the polyhedron by adding increments to individual components of the coordinates and then selecting for improvements.

The results were quite disappointing. The method did not converge except for a small number of variables. The whole *population* of points would tend to evolve such that all points were on one of the hyperplanes forming the boundary of the polyhedron (or at best on the interesection of a few, but not all, hyperplanes going through the solution vertex). Several modifications of this method were tried but brought little improvement. For a more detailed description, see Bremermann-Salaff [7].

4. AN EFFECTIVE METHOD FOR LINEAR PROGRAMMING PROBLEMS

After these experiments a new method was developed that converged in all of the previously attempted cases. This method is described in detail (a flow chart) in Bremermann-Rogson [8] and in Rogson [10]. Intuitively it may be described as follows. A point, $x^{(0)}$, is given in the polyhedron. The intersection, $y^{(0)}$, of the line through $x^{(0)}$ perpendicular to the cost plane, with the boundary of the polyhedron is found. To the vector $x^{(0)} - y^{(0)}$ add a perturbation vector e, multiplied by a factor f. Since the perturbed vectors lie in a cone around $x^{(0)} - y^{(0)}$ f is called the *cone factor*.

Note that fe here takes the place of the increment Δx used in the experiments on linear systems. Each of the components of e may range over a continuum. We discretize the problem by choosing $e = (O, \ldots, 1, \ldots O)$, where all but one of the components are zero. We thus *mutate* the direction $x^{(0)} - y^{(0)}$ by adding increments to individual components. It turned out that the value of the cone factor, f, is quite important. In each experiment a *high* factor and a *low* factor was used, which factors were further multiplied by a uniformly distributed random number.

After generating a *population* of perturbed directions all possible pairs of directions are *mated* (i.e. averaged). For each direction of this new population find the intersection of the line through $x^{(0)}$ (and in the direction under consideration) with the boundary of the polyhedron. From all these intersection points select the one closest to the cost plane. Let this point be $y^{(1)}$. Then iterate the whole procedure, with $x^{(0)} - y^{(1)}$ taking the place of $x^{(0)} - y^{(0)}$. Table 3 summarizes some typical results of these linear programming experiments (as in the previous experiments, the program was in FORTRAN and the computer was an IBM 7090).

TABLE 3

Results of Linear Programming Problems

n	No. of Iterations	Largest Error	T
5	5	0.25	not avail.
5	11	0.21	7.5 sec.
5	10	0.059	7.5 sec.
5	20	0.002	15 sec.
5	19	0.0001	15 sec.
9	10	0.21	30 sec.
9	9	0.07	not avail.
9	30	0.0025	4.5 sec.
10	21	0.077	not avail.
20	218	20.24	15 min.
20	316	15.45	20 min.
30	30	14.50	2.4 min.

As in Table 1, n here denotes the number of variables; *largest error* means the largest coordinate error. The programs terminated either if the difference between two successive improvements was less than a given ϵ, or if the permitted amount of time was exceeded. In order to conserve computer time, most of the experiment was done with small n. It was observed that there was little difference (for the above-described methods) between polyhedra with m boundary planes, $m=n$, and the case $m>n$. For this reason these experiments were carried out for $m = n$. The considerable variation in the *largest error* reported in the table for $n=5$ and $n=9$ is the result of experimenting with the cone factor. For $n=20$ the process seemed to stagnate again. Extensive experiments were not conducted with this case because of the related expense of computer time.

5. LINEAR PROGRAMMING: COMBINED SEXUAL AND ASEXUAL METHOD

To increase efficiency, the method just described was combined with asexual evolution. Each perturbation is immediately tested for improvement and taken to replace $x^{(o)}-y^{(i)}$ if the associated point on the boundary had a lower cost. (In some cases it was specified that the cost improvement had to exceed a given value). This asexual evolution is pursued until it stagnates. Then the program switches to a sexual cycle (the program described in Section 4). If an improvement is obtained, the program switches back to asexual evolution and so on, until no further progress is made. Table 4 summarizes some typical results (this table contains a sampling of our experiments; for a more extensive listing see Rogson[10]).

TABLE 4

Combined Sexual and Asexual Method

n	No. of Iterations	Largest Error	T
5	6	0.01	4.2
5	10	0.00005	7.2
5	4	0.067	1.8
5	4	0.000001	6.0
9	77	0.04	115.8
9	10	0.036	25.8
9	9	0.000027	25.2
10	2	0.133	4.8
10	5	0.001	27.0
10	1	0.127	3.6
20	16	0.17	54.0
20	2	0.28	60.0
20	1	0.19	60.0
30	1	1.2	322.2
30	2	2.4	283.2
30	2	0.5	669

The variability in the largest error and in the time taken is due to experimentation with various parameters entering the program: the cone factors and an *acceptance criterion* number (a number which an asexual improvement has to exceed in order to be accepted). Zero was found to be the best acceptance number, this corresponding to having a *mutant* to replace the *ancestor* if it equals the *cost* (fitness) of the *ancestor*. Moreover, a *population reduction factor* was varied in these experiments which causes the program to select only some pairs (instead of taking all pairs as in Section 4) for mating in the sexual cycle.

This program is obviously more efficient than the program described in Section 4. It handled with considerable success the case of $n=30$ which previously had to be abandoned because it required too much computer time. Asexual improvements played an important role in all the cases listed above. In most cases, however, the program cycled between asexual and sexual phases, with asexual improvements contributing much to convergence, while the sexual cycles seem to keep the program from stagnating.

6. CONVEX PROGRAMMING

The method discussed in Section 5 does not make use of the fact that the convex set (in the following also called *constraint set*) is a polyhedron, other than in determining the intersection of a line (through $x^{(o)}$) with the boundary of the set. When the boundary consists of segments of planes, then the intersection can be computed easily.

In the case of a convex *constraint set* we assume that the set is given by $\{x | \varphi_j(x) > O\}$, j=1, . . . *m* where the functions φ^i are continuous functions. To determine the intersection of such a set with a line, a method was developed that proceeds in steps along the line till it overshoots the boundary, then backs up in smaller steps till it is back in the set, steps forward with smaller steps, etc., until a satisfactory approximation is obtained.

For convenience ellipsoids were used mainly with the case $m = 1$. In some experiments it became apparent that the method also worked for $m > 1$. The effect of the ratio of the axes and the position of the point $x^{(o)}$ was also studied. Obviously, if the ellipsoid is an elongated *cigar,* the problem is more difficult than in the case where the ellipsoid is nearly spherical.

The method did remarkably well even in a case of ellipsoids whose one axis was 100 times or 200 times longer than the other axes. The method also proved remarkably insensitive to the position of $x^{(0)}$. A subroutine that changed $x^{(0)}$ in the course of evolution was abandoned. In most cases it seemed to consume more time than it saved by providing more favorable starting points. Table 5 summarizes some of the experiments (more explicit details, and a flow chart, may be found in Rogson [10]).

TABLE 5

Convex Programming

n	No. of Iterations	Largest Error	Largest Ratio of Axes	T (sec.)
2	1	0	5/3	1.2
2	4	3×10^{-6}	100	3.0
3	3	0	2	1.8
3	4	0.02	200	5.0
4	29	0.002	100	75.6
6	1	0	2	3.6
6	3	0.06	2	16.2
10	5	0.05	2	93.0

Variation in speed and quality of convergence depend upon a number of additional parameters: cone factor, starting point, and position of cost plane relative to main axis of ellipsoid.

7. CONCLUSIONS

After initial frustrations a highly effective search program has been developed. If written in machine language the program could probably be made considerably more efficient. Moreover, in the sexual phase large families of directions are generated at present. At this point considerable economies should be possible. Such an improved program should be able to handle convex programming problems involving 100 variables, and perhaps more. The method does not accumulate roundoff errors. It could be used as a safety check in conjunction with the simplex method.

An attempt will be made to apply the combined *asexual sexual* evolutionary method to problems where the constraint set is not convex. In particular an attempt will be made to find roots of polynomials (in the complex plane) in this way.

There may be lessons of more general importance in the experiments reported here. Evolution is a very basic fact of life. The concept of a *selection advantage* associated with a single gene is valid only in local situations, but not over many generations and many changes in the genotype.

The experiments reported here point to a mathematical challenge: to really understand search processes. For a well defined search problem of a certain type, does there exist an optimal search strategy? Is it possible to estimate the maximum speed with which an optimal strategy will converge?

REFERENCES

1. R. M. Friedberg, "A Learning Machine," *IBM Journal, Research and Development,* Part I, Vol. 2, pp. 2-13, January 1958, Part II, Vol. 3, July, 1959.

2. A. L. Samuel, "Some Studies in Machine Learning Using the Game of Checkers," E. A. Feigenbaum and Julian Feldmann, eds., *Computers and Thought,* pp. 71-105, McGraw-Hill, New York, 1963.

3a. L. J. Fogel, A. J. Owens and M. J. Walsh, "Artificial Intelligence Through the Simulation of Evolution." (these *Proceedings.*)

3b. L. J. Fogel, "Biotechnology: Concepts and Applications," Chapter 10, Prentice-Hall, 1963.

4. H. J. Bremermann, "The Evolution of Intelligence," ONR Technical Report No. 1, Contract NONR 477(17), 1958.

5. H. J. Bremermann, "Optimization Through Evolution and Recombination," *Self-Organizing Systems,* Yovits, Goldstine, Jacobi, eds., Spartan Books, Washington, D. C., 1962.

6. M. Minski, "Steps Towards Artificial Intelligence," *Proc. IRE,* Vol. 49, pp. 3-30, January 1961.

7. H. J. Bremermann and S. Salaff, "Experiments with Patterns of Evolution," ONR Technical Report, Contracts 222(85) and 3656(08), Berkeley, California, November 1963.

8. H. J. Bremermann and M. Rogson, "An Evolution-type Search Method for Convex Sets," ONR Technical Report, Contracts 222(85) and 3656(58), Berkeley, California, May 1964.

9. W. W. Bledsoe, "The Use of Biological Concepts in the Analytical Study of Systems." Panoramic Research, Inc., Technical Reports, 1961.

10. M. Rogson, "A Search Method in Convex Programming," ONR Technical Report, Contracts 222(85) and 3656(08), Berkeley, California, to appear (approximately December 1964).

APPENDIX*

INTRODUCTION

One of the most valuable aspects of the Cybernetic Sciences Symposia is the opportunity provided by a special closing discussion session for critical review and analysis of the material presented by the authors of invited papers, and of related material stimulated during the presentation sessions. In addition to a particularly vigorous discussion of Fogel's paper (as a consequence of which four Commentaries and Fogel's Replies were submitted for publication and appear in this book appended to his paper), a considerable discussion centered on a theme of Louis Fein concerning the utility to biologists of simulations and modeling. Fein submitted a Commentary, to which a number of the participants requested opportunity to respond. Fein's Commentary and eight Responses appear in this Appendix. The expressions of viewpoints in the original papers were frequently militant; the papers have been edited for content as well as syntax.

COMMENTARY

FEIN:† I would like to take this opportunity to express my concern over what I feel is the questionable utility of digital computer program simulations and neural net models, and to request the participants at the Second Cybernetic Sciences Symposium to suggest possible ameliorations of that concern. I am not convinced that the mentioned simulations and/or models have significantly contributed to the resolution of specific issues in neurophysiology or psychology, or have suggested specific formulations

---

* The Editors wish to thank Dr. James Emmett Garvey, ONR/Pasadena, for accepting the responsibility of revising the Commentary and the Responses which appear in this Appendix. [ED.]
† Louis Fein, Consultant, Palo Alto, California.

of questions or problems or a research strategy in these fields. My lack of conviction is a product of serious attention in recent years to the interplay between modeling and simulation on the one hand, and specific biological research problems on the other. I believe that the papers presented at this symposium which were relevant to the stated concern have not considerably modified that concern.

I realize, of course, that my apparent failure to observe certain significant contributions, certain fruitful suggestions, is by no means conclusive. However, it may prove worthwhile to here state an implication which is matured from my concern: perhaps modelers and simulators of physiological and psychological processes and structures should give more consideration to determining the necessary relations that should obtain between their models and what is modeled, in order for models to yield fruitful suggestions and useful information. I would welcome serious comment on this matter by the participants at this symposium.

RESPONSES

GOLD *(Northrup Nortronics):* My knowledge of neurophysiology and psychology is not adequate to allow me to speak with assurance concerning these fields, but from the standpoint of artificial intelligence I agree with Fein without reservation: it is my opinion that neural net simulation has contributed nothing, either in theory or hardware, toward the achievement of artificial intelligence.

In discussing research in general, I similarly believe that a large fraction of the work being performed will never yield useful results. Perhaps one reason for this is that decisions to support or maintain a research project are often based on hoped for future results rather than on a record of past accomplishments.

Neural net modeling does have a positive accomplishment to its credit in the mathematical theory of finite automata: the study of the neuron model of McCulloch and Pitts led Kleene* to introduce and investigate the concept of regular expressions. At that time the McCulloch-Pitts networks were often identified with finite automata. However, they proved to be more cumbersome and less general than the Mealy and Moore definitions of finite automata, and have disappeared from the literature.

In the fields of pattern recognition and computer design, the study of majority logic may have been prompted by neuron models (not neural-*net* simulation), but I am not sure of the history here. However, in pattern

---

* S. C. Kleene, "Representation of Events in Nerve Nets and Finite Automata," in *Automata Studies,* Princeton University Press, 1956.

recognition I have often been of the opinion that neural net simulations have been liabilities. Besides yielding no theoretical insight, the hardware produced has hidden the fact that the problems considered were of a relatively elementary nature and the results might well have been achieved by means of equipment designed in a direct manner. In my experience it has been usually, though not always, the case that direct design converges faster and, moreover, one could predict its rate of convergence in advance.

SALTZBERG *(Bissett-Berman Corp.):* Fein's criticism is refreshingly candid, but, I believe, somewhat out of perspective. His criticism fails to recognize that the early phase of almost every scientific approach is characterized by the groping nature of the theory (in this case, neural network theory), as well as the inadequacy of initial models and simulations. This comment seems especially pertinent when the goal of the research is to shed significant light on neurophysiological or psychological phenomena. Out of this context, however, I do believe Fein's criticism has some validity in somewhat the same sense as it was valid to challenge the practical usefulness of non Euclidean geometry in the 19th century, rather than awaiting the judgment of the 20th century. Thus, this is to suggest that the criticism by Fein is premature, that the discipline is still developing and that some apparently fruitless efforts must form a part, an essential part, of the learning process. Based on material presented at this Symposium, I have considerable appreciation for the difficulties associated with the learning process, as well as a renewed faith in the continuous maturation of the discipline.

FOGEL *(General Dynamics/Astronautics):* I share Fein's concern for the neurophysiologist and the psychologist through the use of mathematical models and/or computer programs, but this concern should not distract attention from the equally important problem of solving engineering problems through the use of such models and/or programs. In particular, our knowledge of biological systems and their behavior may provide conceptual bases for the development of models without there being any specific intent to gain a greater understanding of the biological systems through their exercise. The evolutionary program I referred to in my presentation is a case in point. The primary intent was to solve practical problems. Aspects of evolution are reflected only as a means to this end. Hopefully, this program may also serve to stimulate those who desire to learn more about the process of natural evolution, but this benefit would certainly be a by-product of the original intent. It is likely that investigators in the life sciences may find evolutionary programming to be of greater utility as a means for the prediction of time series and the identification of the degree of relevance of individual variables.

LEWIS *(General Precision/Librascope):* I must begin by agreeing, in principle, with what I understand to be Fein's main thesis: research not based on sound strategy will bear little fruit. I disagree, however, with his implication that all neural modeling falls in this category. His criticism specifically mentions digital computer simulations and neural net models, and it is possible that he is excluding formal models of the nerve membrane (e.g., the Hodgkin/Huxley model), models of single neurons as contrasted to neural nets, and modeling concerned with ganglia. It is conceivable that the real problem is semantics. In any event, it may be of some value to the discourse to comment on some modelers of earlier times, studying their efforts in the framework of the apparent criticism by Fein of nut and bolt, resistor and capacitor, hardware models of neural activity.*

First consider the model *Torpedo* of Henry Cavendish. The shocks delivered by the electric ray (Torpedo) had been known at least since the time of ancient Greece. A number of theories existed to explain these shocks, but electricity was not suggested until the latter half of the eighteenth century. In 1772, John Walsh conducted a series of experiments to determine whether or not the shock was indeed due to electricity. Unfortunately, the shocks did not exhibit all of the known properties of electricity and, in fact, exhibited some properties not yet found in electrical phenomena. The scientific world was left in doubt. At this time Cavendish built a series of model torpedoes. His final model consisted of a shoe leather body separating two plates. The plates were covered with sheepskin and charged from Leyden jars. With this model, Cavendish demonstrated all of the properties observed by Walsh in the real torpedo. This satisfied the scientific community and established *animal electricity* as a fact.

Next consider the work of DuBois-Reymond, some seventy years after Cavendish constructed his model ray, who demonstrated for the first time an electrical phenomenon connected with transmission in nerve. Shortly after this discovery, DuBois-Reymond proposed the *peripolar molecular theory* to explain the pre-existing potential, electronus, and the action potential in nerve. He had tested this hypothesis by means of a series of zinc and copper models. The work with these models led to modifications of his theory and guided much of his research. The *peripolar molecular theory* was short lived, however, because it hinged on pre existing EMF in nerve and this was discredited.

---

*Useful references in this regard include the following: W. Biedermann, *Electrophysiology,* Volume II; Macmillan and Co., Ltd., London, 1898; DuBois-Reymond, *Animal Electricity,* John Churchill, London, 1852; W. Cameron Walter, "Animal Electricity Before Galvani," *Annals of Science, II.* p. 84-113.

Finally, consider the work of Matteucci, who in 1863 *indicated the true physical explanation of electrotonus.* He did this by experimenting with platinum wires soaked in conducting fluids. Experiments with this type of model were continued through the last of the nineteenth century. Hermann, Hering, Frunhagen, and many other physiologists studied electrotonus in artificial systems. These studies had a profound influence on the neurophysiology of the day. Thus, in the dawn of electrophysiology, three physical analogs, or models, played important roles, the first in establishing *animal electricity,* the second in providing one of the first electrical theories of propagation in nerve, and the third in providing a theory of electrotonic spread.

HENDRIX *(Space-General Corporation):* It seems to me that Fein's criticism of computer simulations and/or nerve net models is unduly harsh. We have only just begun this sort of activity; perhaps we should be content to walk a little before we run. Still, one can hardly deny that he is very probably correct when he says such activity has not *as yet* produced much useful output.

If we agree that computer simulations and nerve net theories have not been spectacularly successful, we ought to try to examine the reasons why. I can suggest three.

The first reason is in the complexity of the problem. The more simple biological systems are just beginning to yield to the physicomathematical approach (although I have heard several eminent neurophysiologists argue hotly that such approaches were fruitless—Fein's thesis is not a new one!). Probably the most outstanding of a first rate physical model is the Hodgkin/Huxley theory of the axon. The several journals devoted to biophysics are full of lesser examples. However, when we wish to study less simple systems, we find that the approach via conventional mathematics rapidly fails us and we are left with simulation as our only workable analytical tool. The physical scientist is familiar with this situation. Probably 90 per cent of computer time which is devoted to scientific work today is involved in solving problems which were simply impossible to even consider as recently as two decades ago. The successes which physics and engineering can ascribe to simulation are at least cause for optimism that biology will ultimately be able to make similar progress. That it has not yet done so is only a reflection of the difficulty of the problem.

A second reason for Fein's disappointment may lie in a semantic problem. The great majority of biologists, including some very good ones, simply do not have enough mathematics to understand what the simulation people are talking about. An even greater majority of physicists and engineers are totally illiterate in biology.* If simulation and modeling have not been as successful as they should have been, perhaps this part of the trouble lies in the formulation of the problem. This is, of course, the main point of Fein's comment.

A third reason for lack of perfection in our activities may lie in the digital computer itself. I suspect that this is the most serious and deep lying of the three. When we speak of computers, it is almost a certainy these days that we are speaking of digital computers. Although such devices are often described as *general purpose*, it would be hard to imagine a device more admirably unsuited for neural net simulation. Digital computers, must almost of a necessity, work in sequential fashion, performing one elementary task after another. This necessity has resulted in the speed race, with computer manufacturers vying with one another to see who can build the fastest machine. A neural net, however, is inherently a parallel entity, with a great many elementary operations taking place simultaneously and interacting in complex ways. It is extremely difficult to simulate such inter-actions (feedback, feedforward and feedsideways) in a sequential machine. The more complex the interaction, the slower and clumsier the simulation becomes until the experimenter loses his patience and his financial sponsors their enthusiasm.

I firmly believe that what is needed is a new kind of computer which would in fact simulate a neural net. That is, it would consist of a great many elementary artificial neurons, interconnected in complex ways. The more complex the resulting structure, the more interesting we can expect its behavior to be. This would suggest that our approach should be to design neuron models for small size, low power consumption and, above all, low cost, and to devise ways for interconnecting them. There will be many opinions of what characteristics the ultimate neuron models should have; hopefully, there will be as many different mechanizations as opinions. If this seems to be an engineering rather than scientific approach, I do not apologize. I think it *is* an engineering problem.

In conclusion, I believe Fein's commentary is worthwhile for calling attention to a potential defect in a very new field. And I further believe that the present stage of groping for sound approaches is soon going to yield some very valuable results.

------

* The participants in this Symposium presumably are representative of the minor-ity from each of the disciplines who can speak each other's language more or less fluently. I estimate that the participants number some 10-15% of all the people in the world who are engaged in some kind of neural modeling. Yet, even in this highly selected group, there is evidence of linguistic barriers.

BINGGELI *(University of Southern California):* I respond to Fein's commentary from the point of view of a biologist who is interested in the simulation and modeling of functions which I am just now seriously beginning to approach through typical physiological methods. I believe that Fein's concern may indeed be partly relieved by a reasonable appreciation of the interaction between the Daly-Wolff-Nelson model of the retina and my own biological work on that structure.* Both the biologist and the engineers were involved in a massive literature search of biological data pertinent to the retina which was found to come from a bewildering number of classes of biological research. An attempt was made on the part of the engineers to extract and synthesize from this diverse data information useful for building a semi realistic working model. Simplifying assumptions were demanded by the engineers and criticized by the biologist. Data gaps were presented to the biologist stimulating still further literature search into rare, valuable, and until then unknown (to the group) sources. All of these initial steps and the actual building and initial testing of the model contributed to one valuable end from my perspective, namely, an evaluation of the completeness and adequacy of all previous work done in the field. I feel that in no other way could such a concrete evaluation have been possible.

Up until this time it had not been possible for me to engage in any actual physiological research on the retina. Using the information we had up to that point the model failed to perform well the class of functions in which we were most interested. The model builders kept pressing upon me one particular simplifying assumption which I was reluctant to accept. Not being able to persuade me to permit the adaptation, they then pressed for me to find out whether this assumption were not an actual biological phenomenon. Having exhausted the literature I was strongly bent toward an actual research strategy which I would never have taken without the urging of the modelers. Just within this last month have I been able to begin this investigation. I have been encouraged by the fact that only a few weeks ago J. Z. Young, the prominent British neurophysiologist, in collaboration with the Lettvin, Pitts, Maturana group at MIT, have concluded that in order to explain a certain position vector in the octopus retina they needed to make exactly the same assumption the modelers had proposed to me. The results of my investigation are not complete as yet but if they do bear out the claim of the modelers and Young et al., the credit will be due to the interdisciplinary cooperation between biology, mathematics, and engineering. The project is still in its early phases and as the interaction of actual biological research and model building begins

---

* Binggeli here refers to the model described in Chapter 6 of this book. [ED.]

to occur a more mature evaluation of the productivity of the approach can be made.

PERKEL *(Rand)* and MOORE *(University of California, L. A.):* In response to Fein's commentary on the fruitlessness of simulation and modeling, and in an attempt to relieve his concern, we suggest the following three instances as clear-cut cases of neural models being uniquely useful to research workers in neurophysiology:

(a) The unexpected stability of patterning and the *paradoxical* driving effect of nonreciprocally coupled pacemakers was elucidated first through computer simulations and associated mathematical analysis[1]. The stable firing patterns of pacemaker inhibited pacemakers, except for the one to one pattern, were looked for and first noticed in previously obtained intracellular recordings in *Aplysia* only after they had been predicted by computer. The results of Schulman's crayfish experiment[2], in which inhibitory frequency was varied, had been predicted independently (although probably not beforehand) by the computer model.

(b) According to a personal communication from Prof. T. H. Bullock, some modes of activity in coelenterate nerve nets were first suggested by the results of computations on a digital-computer nerve-net model[3], and later observed in living animals. Elaborations of this program are at present in continuous and active use in Prof. Bullock's laboratory[4], where they serve to extend, elaborate, and guide experimental programs.

(c) L. D. Harmon's electronic analog neural model, the neuromine, has been at least of suggestive value to D. M. Wilson in proposing mechanisms underlying neural control of insect flight: ". . . Wilson had just demonstrated that a novel input-output firing characteristic predicted by earlier experiments with neuromines indeed held under some conditions for real neurons." [5] "The phenomenon . . . has been studied intensively with electronic model systems. . . . Harmon describes a process, hitherto unknown in the nervous system. . . . The same phenomenon has been identified now in the locust nervous system. . . . Some old records . . . also show the . . . phenomenon. I was unable to interpret them at the time they were made."[6]

It is, of course, difficult to ferret out from published reports the precise source of an experimenter's inspiration or interpretation. In practice, we have found both *real* and computer experiments to be sources of fruitful ideas. The computer experiments have not only predicted phenomena actually observed in the laboratory, but in addition—and probably more importantly—have predicted the behavior of neurons under conditions that we have not yet had the opportunity to confirm in living preparations. Models are extremely useful in extending the range of experiments beyond the inherent constraints imposed by an experimental arrangement and under a variety of circumstances that are difficult to arrange *ad libitum* in the living animal.

The most significant use of neural models, analog or digital, is a heuristic one: effectively used, they suggest possibilities; they encourage the enumeration of specific alternatives; they force the precise specification of alternative hypotheses; and they serve as an ideal tool for the elaboration of the consequences of hypotheses; in short, they furnish a vehicle for the application of the *principle of strong inference* so essential to sustained scientific progress.[7]

A vehicle must be driven by a competent driver. Effective exploitation of the power of models requires continual interplay between experimenter, model, and model maker; the requisite communications channels are slow and sometimes painful to set up. While neurophysiological modelling by digital or electronic analog computer has not yet substantiated all the claims made for it (it has not yet affected experimental neurophysiology in a dramatic or sizable way) we question the value of Fein's comments regarding the relative fruitlessness of simulation and modeling. If there are *bad* models, that is, unrealistic, over or undersimplified, or grossly uneconomical models, they have not to our knowledge been constructed with the active advice and participation of imaginative experimental biologists. If *good* models are being ineffectively exploited, we attribute this to the relatively small amount of experience by biologists in using these models; that experience is of course growing both in depth and range. If through defective models or ineffective exploitation there are modeling activities which are indeed unproductive, as Fein alleges, the remedy, we submit, lies not in Fein's *conditions* but rather in a more intense and detailed investigation, application, and improvement of the models themselves by experimental neurophysiologists.

The intent of our models is to aid in the furtherance of scientific understanding of neural systems. We can only reiterate that intent for the kinds of neural models and applications represented, for example, by our own models, those of Josephson, Reiss and Worthy, those of E. R. Lewis[8], and those of L. D. Harmon.

REFERENCES (to PERKEL and MOORE RESPONSE)

1. G. P. Moore, J. P. Segundo, and D. H. Perkel, "Stability Patterns in Interneuronal Pacemaker Regulation," *Proceedings of the San Diego Symposium for Biomedical Engineering,* A. Paull, Ed., La Jolla, Calif., 1963, pp. 184-193.

2. D. H. Perkel, J. H. Schulman, T. H. Bullock, G. P. Moore, and J. P. Segundo, "Pacemaker Neurons: Effects of Regularly Spaced Synaptic Input," *Science* 145, 1964, pp. 61-63.

3. R. K. Josephson, R. F. Reiss, and R. M. Worthy, "A Simulation Study of a Diffuse Conducting System Based on Coelenterate Nerve Nets," *J. Theoret. Biol.* 1, 1961, pp. 460-487.

4. In the Department of Zoology, University of California, Los Angeles.

5. L. D. Harmon, "Neuromimes: Action of a Reciprocally Inhibitory Pair," *Science* 146, 1964, pp. 1323-1325.

6. D. M. Wilson, "Relative Refractoriness and Patterned Discharge of Locust Flight Motor Neurons," *J. Exptl. Biol.* 41, 1964, pp. 191-205.

7. J. R. Platt, "Strong Inference," *Science* 146, 1964, pp. 347-353.

8. E. R. Lewis, "An Electronic Analog of the Neuron Based on the Dynamic of Potassium and Sodium Fluxes," *Neural Theory and Modeling,* R. F. Reiss, Ed., Stanford University Press, Palo Alto, Calif., 1964.

ROBERT M. STEWART *(Space-General Corporation)* Louis Fein, well-known critic,[1] humorist,[2] and economic theorist,[3] strikes again, this time registering disappointment in the methods and accomplishments of our strange confederation, The Grand Army of Cyberneticists. Since he has singled out digital computer simulations and models for criticism, and since our own work is concerned instead with physical analogues of excitability and growth, his stated "concern" may or may not extend to us. But these comments seem to reflect a common confusion of method, progress and purpose in contemporary science and a basic misunderstanding of the role of models.[4] Model techniques, mathematical and otherwise, contribute most to the process of exploration and discovery in nature by providing versatile and novel means for framing hypotheses which *may* reveal order in seemingly chaotic and disparate fields of imperfect and incomplete data. The extent to which they *ultimately* prove able to do this is normally taken to indicate the relative significance of the model. Hopefully, the extent and manner in which they fail can also often be used as a guide to further refinements or new approaches. History shows that, except for trivial cases, this is a slow and painful process, full of trial-and-error and the sharpening of new tools on knowingly oversimplified but tractable exercises, and one whose success can never, as Fein demands, be guaranteed a priori. Recognition of the present state of total ignorance concerning the actual physiological mechanisms of logic, memory and learning in the human brain suggests that this describes quite accurately the contemporary position of neurophysiology; and it is to be hoped that the continued development of the tools of cybernetic science, accompanied by a steadily improving dialogue with the biologists may eventually provide conceptual frameworks that will aid in the attack on these problems. Even though I share Fein's impatience, none of us is at present in a position to issue blanket condemnations or legislate Method Science. Fashions in biological theory tend to reflect currently available experimental technique and procedures. Such theory will be found to be inadequate insofar as these observations prove to be extraneous or irrelevant to an understanding of the integrative functions of the brain; for example, all the microscopic magnification in the world focused on the synaptic cleft will not shed light on possible cellular interaction mechanisms which implicate electrical fields extending *throughout* each cell or cell assembly; all of the analytical chemistry in the world will not solve the memory problem if, in fact, the memory substrate or engram resides in the intricacies of cellular structure rather than in molecular structures; and there is little hope of advancing our understanding of pain and pleasure if we have no alternative other than to picture the brain as a miniature digital computer, a set of recursion formulae, or a hat full of DNA. Fein may accurately reflect the attitude of applications engineering[5], but he is way out of line in attempting to blow the biological science side of the cybernetic house down even before the building bricks have been delivered.

Since Fein is looking for "specific formulations of questions or problems or a research strategy" in neurophysiology or psychology, he might start by considering the electrical model of excitatory and inhibitory coupling between electrochemical bipolar cells which we have previously described [6,7] and our proposal and demonstration that membrane impedance drop following excitation may play an essential role in temporally associative learning.[7,8] But he will be disappointed if he expects much immediate help from physiologists or psychologists in correctly assaying the validity of these models; in the light of existing data they are plausible, but because of the extensive electrical fields involved, contemporary in vivo experimental technique is not adequate to perform a definitive test. We believe that, with the aid of electrochemical model techniques, applied to complex cell assemblies, we may eventually be able to suggest indirect tests and critical comparisons based on accessible observations. We can only hope that such suggestions will elicit informed and specific consideration rather than critical vagaries.

REFERENCES (to STEWART RESPONSE)

1. L. Fein, "The Artificial Intelligentsia," *IEEE Spectrum*, Volume 1, Number 2, February 1964, pp. 74-87.
2. ———, "The Computer-Related Sciences (Synnoetics) at a University in the Year 1975," *American Scientist*, Volume 49, Number 2, June 1961.
3. ———, "Dear Mr. President," *Datamation*, January 1965, p. 39.
4. J. Z. Young, *Doubt and Certainty in Science*, Oxford University Press, New York, 1960.
5. L. Fein, "Figure of Merit for Evaluating Control Computer System," *Automatic Control*, v. 12, 5, May 1960, pp. 39-41.
   ———, "Suitable Applications for Computers Built of Kilomegacycle Memory and Logic Componentry," AIEE Special Pub. S-136, January 1962, No. 17.
   ———, "Assessing Computing Systems," IEEE Special Publ. S-143, January 1963, pp. 6-8.
6. R. M. Stewart, "Adaptable Cellular Nets," *Progress in Biocybernetics*, v. 1, Eds. Wiener and Schade, Elsevier, Amsterdam, 1964, pp. 96-105.
7. ———, "Fields and Waves in Excitable Cellular Structures," Proceedings First Pasadena Invitational Symposium of Self-Organizing Systems, Office of Naval Research Department of the Navy, Washington, D. C.
8. ———, "Learning Systems In and Out of the Factory," 1964, WESCON, Los Angeles, Calif., Paper No. 3.4.

Index

184